METRO
THE BOOK OF THE CAR

METRO
THE BOOK OF THE CAR

Graham Robson

Foreword by Harold Musgrove

Chairman, Austin Rover Group Limited

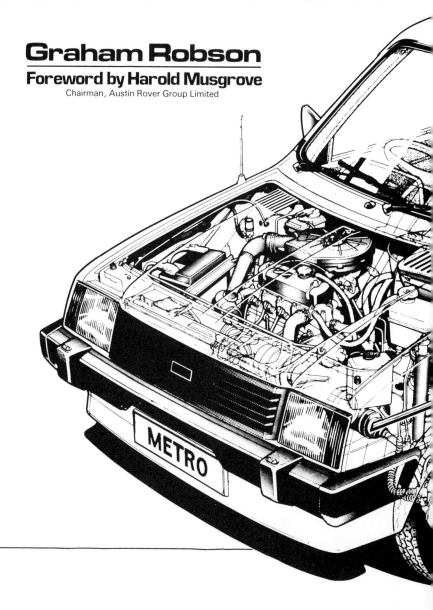

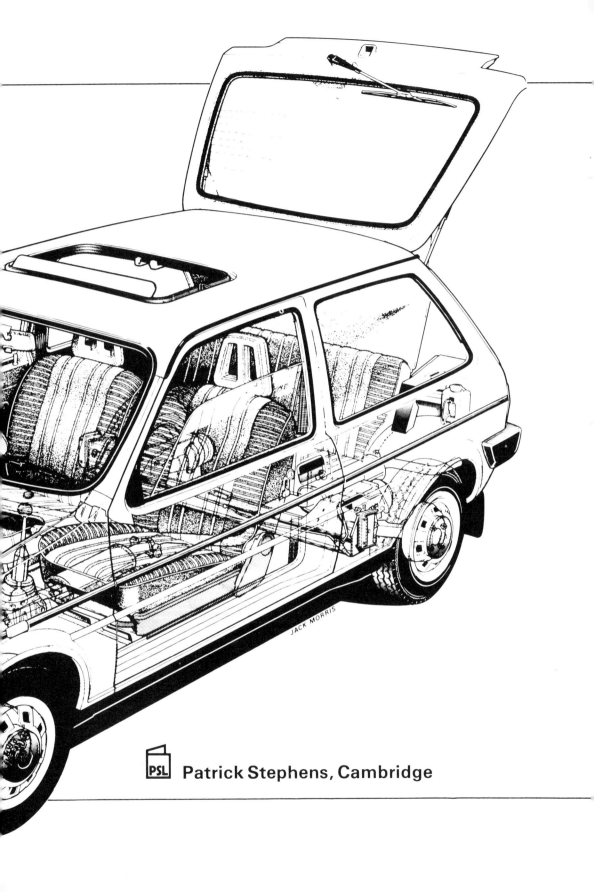

JACK MORRIS

PSL **Patrick Stephens, Cambridge**

Title page *The £270 million skeleton of Metro, as put on sale in 1980. It was a miracle of good packaging, in a practical, no-nonsense layout.*

© Graham Robson 1982

First published in 1982

British Library Cataloguing in Publication Data

Robson, Graham
   Metro.
   1. Mini Metro automobile—History
   I. Title
   629.2'222   TL215.M/

   ISBN 0-85059 593-2

Photoset in 10 on 11 pt Garamond by Manuset Limited, Baldock, Herts. Printed in Great Britain on 115 gsm Fineblade coated cartridge by R.J. Acford Ltd, Chichester, and bound by The Garden City Press, Letchworth, Herts, for the publishers, Patrick Stephens Limited, Bar Hill, Cambridge, CB3 8EL, England.

Contents

Foreword by Harold Musgrove
Chairman, Austin Rover Group Limited

I was particularly delighted to accept Graham Robson's invitation to write this short Foreword to the book of the Metro because it gave me the opportunity to pay my personal tribute to the thousands of my colleagues whose dedication and sheer hard work made the Metro the success story it turned out to be.

Without doubt, the events so carefully chronicled in this book proved to be the most exciting in my working life; for me—and many, many others—the Metro project is a lasting memory I will never forget. I was proud to work alongside some of the finest people in the motor industry—people who had removed the word 'impossible' from the dictionary.

I must also add that at no time during the project did I ever have cause to criticise the employees at Longbridge. As a workforce I regard them amongst the finest car makers in the world today. It must also be recorded that the Metro 'miracle' would not have happened at all had it not been for the truly fantastic support that we received from Sir Michael Edwardes and Ray Horrocks. Once major decisions had been taken, they were not afraid to see them implemented—I just had to make doubly sure that we hit all our targets.

Sir Michael once asked me if I was worried by the responsibility. 'Yes', I said, 'but I would be more worried if I were in your shoes. At least I know what is happening on a day to day basis'.

Looking back now, it still seems truly amazing that everyone hit their targets bang on time—and the whole £270 million programme was achieved within budget. Naturally we hit problems—many of them are faithfully recorded in the chapters of this book. But everyone refused to accept them as problems—they were just challenges to be met head-on and beaten. We all knew Metro had to be successful—not only because it was the most anticipated new car in the history of the UK motor industry, but because it was also seen as the start of BL's product-led recovery in the 1980s. We all had to prove we were capable of producing a world-beater—and we were not to be disappointed.

As Graham Robson records in great detail, the commitment of my colleagues was only matched by the impact of the launch itself. The future of the Metro—just like any other product—is, of course, in the hands of the buying public. For our part, Austin Rover group will continue to produce a superb—and growing—range of

One of the two synchronised robot welding lines for the Metro.

Metro models. It is my personal belief, however, that with such an outstanding basic design, the future of the Metro is assured for many years to come.

HAROLD MUSGROVE
June 1982

Introduction

This is a story that had to be written one day and I always wanted to write it. Well before the Metro was even ready to be revealed, it was already clear that public interest in the project was phenomenal. Nearly a year before the car was scheduled to meet its public, a BL executive told his colleagues: 'Metro is perhaps the most anticipated new car in the history of the UK motor industry'. That, if anything, was an understatement for, not to put too fine a point on it, the entire future of BL Cars. Ltd was riding on the back of this one, £270 million, project.

Because British Leyland had effectively been nationalised in 1975, its future plans were then exposed to a great deal of public scrutiny. BL's plan to develop a new small car, a Supermini, or a 'Mighty Mini' as it became known, became something of an open secret two, or even three, years before BL were ready to start selling it to the public.

It was a car for which everything might go wrong, or for which everything might go triumphantly right, and I wanted to chronicle progress as it took place behind closed doors. In the event, I wasn't able to do that, for the staff of BL Cars wanted to see the car on to the market, to let the dust settle, and to let it prove itself in the showrooms, before they opened too many doors, and exposed too many secrets.

Now, my chance has come. Two years after the Metro was originally announced in October 1980, well over 300,000 have been built and sold. It has consistently exceeded the company forecasts made for it and the derivatives now being launched in some profusion are making the design more attractive to even more people. The little hatchback is a success by any standards.

For the very first time, I believe, this is the *complete* story of the Metro project, not just the well-publicised highlights we have seen so often before. It is a story which not only encompasses the wonderful reception given to the car by the media in October 1980, but the terrifying disappointment of the poor showing of the ADO88 prototypes at 'clinic' in 1977. It is a story which, I hope, restores the reputation of the Longbridge workforce to its rightful place, not only for the way they accepted new working practices to build the Metro, but for the way they kept on building Minis and Allegros as the massive rebuilding of Longbridge proceeded, continuously, about their ears.

It is a story, too, not just stuffed full of technical and marketing facts, but one which has its humorous side as well. It includes the little-known fact that highly expensive machinery being delivered to Longbridge was damaged when the lorry-borne casing hit a bridge on the way to the factory, which nobody knew about until they tried to assemble the parts. It recalls how the chairman's chauffeur-driven Jaguar was used to ferry bacon sandwiches from nearby transport cafés to midnight crisis meetings. There was the fire at Longbridge which destroyed priceless prototypes, and there were the so-called magazine 'scoops' where the wrong car was exposed!

It is a story, still unfolding, which exposes remarkable efforts of human endeavour—like the way in which the entire style and concept of the car was changed in six weeks (towards the end of 1977); how workers turned out over Christmas, in the snow, to rectify faulty conveyors which threatened to close down Longbridge completely; how 100-hour working weeks became common among key staff and workers, and how the whole project stayed precisely, and triumphantly, on target.

As one senior Product Planner told me when I was assembling material: 'We've been on a war footing at BL Cars for years now'. It's a good metaphor. But has the war been won yet? Perhaps it isn't clear, but the battles are being won and the last major defeats may now be in the past. And if the war—the battle for survival at BL— has been won, the Metro was the first major project to make it possible.

Acknowledgements

Writing this book without consulting BL Cars would have been possible, but rather pointless, as I would have had access to only one part of the story. To talk to the people who had been involved from ADO74 and ADO88 days, I needed help and approval from the company and, once I explained my needs, it was always given. The Public Affairs staff, led by Murray Loake, David Boole and Norman Childs, made sure that I talked to the right people, saw the best written material and browsed through mountains of photographs.

I couldn't possibly name everyone in BL, for my researches spread far and wide, but in particular I want to thank busy directors like Harold Musgrove, Tony Gilroy and Tony Ball for recalling the period in the late 1970s when BL Cars was literally fighting for its survival. Rex Fleming and Harris Mann tore themselves away from styling work on LM10 to lead me through the tangled labyrinth of the shaping of ADO88 and LC8, while Stephen Schlemmer of Product Planning told me how the car's range was settled and how the new derivatives took shape. Much of the recollection of design work came from Fred Coultas, John Wheatley and John Benson, while David Boole himself told me a lot about the strategy behind the launch, and marketing, of the first Metros in 1980.

Almost all the photographs are from BL themselves (some from the secret 'prototype' files which are rarely allowed out of captivity), but those referring to the 5,000-miles-in-five-days run are from *Autocar* magazine. To Ray Hutton and his assistant, Warren Allport, as ever, my grateful thanks.

To see fair play, BL staff read the completed manuscript, and put me right on one or two misunderstood details, but I must emphasise that at no time were any facts, or controversial details, suppressed. As far as I know, there isn't a single tall story in the book, even though I have picked up a few along the way . . ..

I could not have done it all on my own. To everyone who helped me build up the story of the concept, development and initial production of the Metro, many thanks. Will there be similar new-product stories to be told about other BL cars in the next few years?

GRAHAM ROBSON

Chapter 1

The Mini phenomenon
The car that started it all

Picture the scene at Longbridge, the vast 'Austin' factory to the south of Birmingham, with a workforce of thousands. Production is high, but profitability is not. Existing products look old-fashioned, there isn't a true mass-market 'baby' car among them, and company morale is low. The future prospects are grim. Help, however, is on the way. Behind closed doors, a tiny new car is being developed—quite different from anything so far seen at Longbridge. In the nick of time, in true Hollywood-thriller style, it bursts on to the scene. The press love it, and the motoring public hail it as a winner. There is a rush to place orders, demand is enormous, and optimism returns to the business. Production lines, foundries, press shops, trim departments and despatch bays all hum with vigorous activity. Profitability returns, and the doom merchants are sent packing.

1980, the birth of the Metro? Certainly not. I'm talking about the Longbridge of 1922, when the *original* Austin mini-car, the Austin Seven, made its bow! I wanted to start my Metro story with a parable which shows that history tends to repeat itself. Not once, but several times in the past, the car-making complex at Longbridge has been in trouble. In 1922, in 1951, and again in 1959, it was the arrival of a new small car which revived the situation.

'When planning your future, first study your past'. Not a famous quotation, perhaps, for I have just invented it, but very appropriate to the long-running story of Austin, Longbridge and the cars built there. The effort put behind the development of the Metro, a car which not only transformed the prospects of the Longbridge factory, but of the entire BL Cars business itself, was immense, but it was not unique. As far as Longbridge was concerned, it had all happened before.

So where can we find the *real* roots of the Metro? In 1978, when the LC8 project was finally approved? A few years earlier, when the first ADO88 sketches were made? In 1959, even, when the pragmatic genius of Alec Issigonis produced the original Mini? My own view is that we have to go all the way back to 1922, to Austin's first financial crisis, and to the design of the Austin Seven.

Whether the car was actually designed on Sir Herbert Austin's billiard table at Lickey Grange, or whether he had as much direct influence on the design as has often been suggested, is no longer important. The really significant fact is that the Austin Seven of 1922 was the first proper 'baby' Austin—there had been a 7 hp car in 1910 which achieved very little.

The Austin Seven was produced at great speed to meet an enormous crisis in the Austin company's affairs. After the end of the First World War, production was concentrated on a big and costly 20 hp model which never sold as well as hoped. Profits of £358,000 in 1918 plummeted to a loss of £2,334,000 in 1921 and a receiver had to be called in.

Sir Herbert, who was proprietor, managing director *and* technical director before the crisis erupted, lost control of his own business for a time, but busied himself with the design of new cars. First came the 12/4, really a scaled-down 20 hp model and next came the legendary Austin Seven. Sir Herbert apparently sketched almost all the design, but it was young Stanley Edge who made the proper engineering drawings.

Sir Herbert's intention was to find a completely new market—to make motorists out of people previously happy to run motor cycle combinations. He even went so far as to address a gathering of motor cycle enthusiasts and say that his new (still-secret) car would knock their products 'into a cocked hat'. He was right. Once the Austin Seven actually went on sale in 1923, it began to break all records. By 1926 it was the largest-selling Austin car, and by 1927 the accumulated losses of the early 1920s had been wiped off for good and all.

Thereafter, there was always a small car to dominate the scene at Longbridge and the business came to rely on having one. The more I look back at the great days of the Austin Seven, and of the cars which eventually took over from it, the more parallels I see. The Austin Seven, like the original Mini, soldiered on for far too long without being radically improved. The Austin Seven, like the Mini, eventually became 'part of the furniture' at Longbridge, so that long-established staff tended to ignore it and its increasing old age. The Austin Seven, like the Mini, also seemed to generate a great deal of buyers' emotion—which made the task of replacing it even more difficult. More and more parallels like this can be defined, in stark contrast to other developments at the rambling old factory on the Longbridge site.

For several years, the Austin Seven was the only ultra-small British car, just as the Mini was the only ultra-small front-wheel-drive car in the country for some time in the 1960s. The opposition—Morris, Ford and Standard in the case of the Austin Seven; Ford, Vauxhall, Rootes and Standard-Triumph in the case of the Mini—eventually produced competing models, after which the battle became increasingly bitter.

The problem was that, having taken the initiative with the remarkable little Austin Seven, the Austin company gradually but definitely lost their way. At first they could find no way of replacing the car, and eventually they became obsessed with the idea of doing so. The car died in 1939, but the name was never allowed to rest. When the little A30 came along in 1951, it was called the 'Austin Seven' at first, and when the first Austin-badged Mini of 1959 arrived it was also advertised as an Austin Seven. The public were not impressed, and would not use the traditional title. An A30 was an A30 as far as they were concerned, and the little front-wheel-drive car was, quite simply, a Mini.

When Longbridge opened up again after the Second World War, Lord Austin was dead, and so was the Austin Seven. Leonard Lord was the company's new supremo, and for a time he concentrated on developing cars to sell overseas. There was no new small Austin until 1951, and even then it was built as much to compete head-on with the Morris Minor, as to produce a profit opportunity for the Austin company.

Times, however, were changing. Austin was large, and getting larger, but so were the problems piling up for the future. In spite of the fact that there was no love lost between Austin and Morris, Leonard Lord was convinced that a merger would one day be needed to found a real colossus fit to tackle any other car-making concern outside North America. The first tentative steps took place in 1948 and 1949, but a full-blooded merger was delayed until the winter of 1951/1952. Without the three-year delay, two things might not have happened—Leonard Lord might not have launched the A30, and the first of the huge Car Assembly Buildings (CAB1), sited on the old airfield south of the old factory buildings, might not have been built.

Thus it was that the British Motor Corporation was formed and—if only we had known it—thus it was that the seeds of eventual financial disaster in British Leyland were sown. In the next few years Lord, who became Sir Leonard in 1954, set about rationalising BMC's use of engines and transmissions, but did little to cut down the number of models. It was not until the late 1950s, with the controversial Farina-styled mid-range saloons, that 'badge-engineering' of a single body shell began in earnest.

In the meantime, inter-company competition between Austin and Morris was as vigorous as ever, even though BMC, and its money-making efforts, seemed to thrive on it. Alec Issigonis, a Briton with a Bavarian mother, had risen rapidly through the engineering heirarchy since joining Morris Motors from the Rootes Group in 1936. During the Second World War, and in conjunction with Sir Miles Thomas (Vice-Chairman of the Nuffield Group), Issigonis had created the Morris 'Mosquito' prototype, a project which evolved into the well-loved Morris Minor of 1948. Other projects were then on the way, but Issigonis tired of inter-factory politicking which followed the Austin-Nuffield merger, and defected to Alvis of Coventry, to spend

The father of all true mini cars—Sir Alec Issigonis—at the wheel of one of the first BMC Minis.

four years designing a 3½-litre V8-engined sports saloon. Before leaving Cowley, however, Issigonis and his team had found time to build a very special experimental Morris Minor—a remarkably prophetic device, with a transversely-mounted four-cylinder engine and front-wheel-drive!

By the beginning of 1956, however, Sir Leonard Lord was restlessly looking around for new designs. His BMC combine was prospering for the moment, but was building a remarkable number of truly turgid cars. Sir Leonard could see that the tide was on the turn, that styling and advanced engineering would soon be the touchstones to selling new cars and that continental designers (in particular Fiat and Renault) were overtaking BMC. Accordingly, he attracted Alec Issigonis away from Alvis, where his ambitious project had just been cancelled for lack of funds, installed him and a small team in a small design office near to his own, and set him to work as BMC's 'think tank'.

For a time, Issigonis and his tiny department was quite separate from the main BMC design effort. All his demands for facilities went direct to Sir Leonard Lord, BMC's chairman, who looked on the work as his own personal fiefdom. It was a classic case of the overgrown schoolboy playing with his toys. (Who was it who said: 'As you get older, nothing changes. The toys just get bigger'?). The first major project, indeed, was coded XC9001, a car which looked rather like the Morris 1100 of the 1960s, but it had a 1½-litre all-aluminium engine driving the back wheels. The most forward-looking feature was the use of Moulton Hydrolastic suspension units, which Issigonis had first used in his still-born Alvis.

The Suez crisis of 1956 changed everything. BMC had just introduced the up-engined Austin A35 and Morris Minor 1000 models, and were feeling very pleased with themselves, when the British and French armies invaded Egypt to reverse the process by which Colonel Nasser had nationalised the Suez canal. The result was opprobrium for Britain and France, nothing but a sound telling-off for Egypt and fuel shortages all round the world for several months. It also spurred on Len Lord to a great new desire—that BMC should produce a very economical and completely different baby car. Sir Leonard never had any doubts that Alec Issigonis was the right man to do the job for him.

Perhaps we should not blame Colonel Nasser and fuel rationing entirely for the need to develop new BMC mini-cars, for the European design-tide was already swinging strongly in that direction already. In particular, Fiat had already launched the Fiat 600 and they were already preparing to add an even smaller machine, the Fiat 500 (the 'new Topolino') to that. No matter. It was the Suez crisis, and the nasty rash of *foreign* bubble-cars which followed, which finally convinced the dynamic chairman. Issigonis was told to drop everything and to design a new very small car. There was only one restriction—that BMC could not afford the time, nor the money, to produce a new engine for the purpose. Legend has it that Sir Leonard's terse instruction was: 'You can use any sort of engine you like so long as we have it on our present production lines'.

Thus it was that in March 1957 the Mini project was born. XC9001 and XC9002 were cancelled and never revived. In their place came the new car, XC9003 at first, and ADO15 once it had become an official project. Quite suddenly, from running the chairman's 'Executive toys' department, Alec Issigonis had become the most important designer in the Corporation.

I should pause, at this point, to apologise for the use of so many project codes instead of vehicle names, but this is inevitable as the motor industry tends to work

The original BMC Mini mock-up, still coded XC 9003. All other Minis, and eventually the Mini Metro, stemmed from this layout.

like that. Later on, we will be tripping over lots more ADO numbers, and will eventually find our first 'LC' number—it is all a part of the jargon used by BL/BMC planners when talking among themselves.

What was XC? Who knows? If it was anything, it stood for Experimental Car design, no more and no less, with the number being added to distinguish it from the next project. ADO. . . is easier to explain. When the Austin and Nuffield design offices were gradually merged in the early 1950s, major new projects were given codes for identification—ADO 6, ADO 8 and so on. ADO stood either for Austin Drawing Office, or for Amalgamated Drawing Office (no one ever bothered to explain), and the numbers were issued in somewhat random order. As far as I can see, the earliest number was ADO 6, which applied to the taxicab range, but there was quite deliberately no logical way in which the numbers were allocated. ADO 37, for instance, applied to the big Vanden Plas 3-litre cars announced at the same time as the Mini, while ADO 14 applied to the Austin Maxi, which didn't arrive until ten years later.

The new baby car—XC9003, ADO 15, call it what you like—had to be tiny, had to be produced as rapidly as possible and had to be fuel efficient. Meeting those requirements was like squaring the circle—in other words, it was extremely difficult—and since there was no such department as Product Planning in BMC at that time, Alec Issigonis had to make all his own decisions. Sir Leonard Lord and his deputy, George Harriman, left him alone to get on with it.

It is now a matter of history, and of great pride at Longbridge, that Issigonis not only did the job in time, but that he did it magnificently. There is no question of him being credited with the first use of front-wheel-drive, or even with the use of a transverse engine, but no one had done it so elegantly, and so compactly, ever before. DKW had been building front-wheel-drive cars since the 1930s, as had Citroën, BSA and others. Saab had joined in from 1950, along with Panhard and others. None of them, however, were space-efficient machines and none used a *four*-cylinder engine set across the structure of the car.

It was the transverse engine, coupled to its ingenious use of the 'gearbox-in-sump' transmission, which was the breakthrough. Issigonis, by his own admission, realised that his four passengers needed to be allocated in a car 8 feet 9 inches long and 4 feet 2 inches wide before allowing space for the engine itself. He was already determined to use a front-engine/front-drive layout (because he didn't like the handling and stability problems associated with the use of a rear engine) and he wanted a really tiny car. There was no point in using a conventional engine layout if his new car was going to be very little shorter than the A35's 11 feet 4 inches. Logically, therefore, the transverse engine was almost forced upon him.

Issigonis, however, was a logical thinker above all and was not about to rest on his laurels after one flash of genius. Lesser designers would not even have thought things through in such a brilliant way, but Issigonis was not content. The design which resulted was not only smaller than any previous *real* British car, at 10 feet 0 inches, but it was also one of the most space efficient ever built. In modern terms, it had a mangificent 'package', where hardly an inch was wasted in any direction. It was easy enough to accept one phrase—that it was larger inside than out—but who was it who first suggested that a Mini was 'like a telephone box on the outside, and the Albert Hall on the inside'? Apart from that, there was the rubber suspension, the squat stance, and the magnificent roadholding, not to mention the fact that it could be

Early front-wheel-drive transverse-engined Mini prototypes used Austin A35 grilles for partial disguise. Industrial espionage was not as highly developed in those days!

parked on a sixpence, and could outrun cars of twice or even three times its engine size. Above all, however, there was its cheeky and endearing character, something which could never have been designed in to it by a cold-blooded executive decision. No one ever drove a Mini and remained indifferent to it—they either loved it, or hated it. I loved my first Mini for its behaviour, and hated it for the way it leaked water—often at one and the same time.

With no more than minimal help from the styling studios at Cowley (not, please note, from Longbridge), Alec Issigonis' team had a car mocked up by July 1957 and the two prototypes running by October. For the next nine months, road work, and proving, went ahead at great speed and, in July 1958, Sir Leonard Lord gave the car his approval after a five-minute run around the factory roads of Longbridge. Within a year the first production cars had been assembled and at the end of August 1959 the public was introduced to them. The age of the Mini had arrived.

This, however, was BMC, at a time when nothing was ever simple. The Austin-Nuffield rivalry was still intense, so both factions had to be satisfied. Both had to have a hand in building the cars, and both had to have derivatives of their own to sell. Right from the start there were to be Austin and Morris versions, and right from the start they were to be assembled at Cowley and Longbridge. To complicate things even further, *some* Austins were built at the old Morris factory at Cowley, while *some* Morris examples took shape at Longbridge. Once production got under way with a vengeance, body shells seemed to come from all over the place—some from Pressed Steel Co, across the road from the Morris factory at Cowley, some from the Fisher & Ludlow factory in Birmingham and some from the Longbridge factory itself.

Tradition, too, had to be satisfied. Austin dealers got a car which was called an Austin Seven at first (the second attempt by Austin to revive that historic name), while Morris dealers had the same car with different badging, known as the Morris Mini Minor. The link with the famous Morris Minor is obvious, but the origins of 'Mini' are more obscure. For sure, Pat Moss, that formidably talented lady rally driver of the 1950s and 1960s, once reported to her service crew in Italy that she had nearly crashed her Morris Minor rally car into a VW Minibus, and that if so, she would have been driving a 'Morris Mini Minor', but no one now knows if that was the origin of the title.

The public, as ever, made up its own mind. Over the years, as the range grew, inter-bred, and became more and more diverse, the original titles were swept away. A Mini was a Mini was a Mini—the hot versions were popularly known as Cooper-Minis, and the Wolseley Hornet version soon became known as a Wolseley Mini. The car made its own name and settled its own reputation.

Getting it on sale, and into production, was a rushed and somewhat shambolic operation. Even though there were dozens of cars to be lent out to influential journalists for long-term tests (it was unfortunate, perhaps, that all these cars had GFC . . . registration numbers, and that one wag said: 'GFC, ah yes, Gifts for Correspondents'), and even though there were cars to sell right away, a host of teething troubles had to be solved. There was the famous water leak problem (carpets tended to float away if not watched), the mysterious case of the clogging up of petrol pumps by ginger hairs (traced to the way the fuel tank pressings were being wiped down in manufacture) and the first cruel jokes ('Keep the side windows closed at all times, in case an Alsatian dog comes along and lifts its leg against the side . . .').

There were also the real triumphs. Straight away, Mini owners began to race their cars, to rally them and to bustle them around the pylons of driving tests. An early tendency to cast off wheels was cured by providing extra-sturdy competition examples and from that point on the cars' reputation improved dramatically. All the tuners knew the A-Series engine inside-out already, so they had no difficulty in making the standard 848 cc short-stroke engine produce a lot more power. It was common knowledge, in any case, that the very first Issigonis prototypes had featured 948 cc engines, and had clocked up 92 mph on test. Once John Cooper, of Grand Prix fame, had got his hands on a car, modified it considerably, and persuaded BMC to put a 997 cc Mini-Cooper into production, the sky was the limit.

Although the sales force were delighted, Alec Issigonis was not always visibly as impressed. In his mind, when designing the Mini, he had always been trying to provide marginal motoring, for the family which might otherwise not have a car at all, or which might be forced to buy some nasty foreign concoction. He wanted it to be a working-class car, for a working-class market. It didn't happen that way, which is probably as well, for the demand would surely never have been as high if it had?

Sir Leonard Lord, BMC and Issigonis did no basic market research before they launched the car and merely built it down to the three basic requirements of minimum size, minimum cost and maximum fuel efficiency. The fact that the car looked good, handled like a thoroughbred, and felt more sporting than any proper sports car in the BMC range, was pure chance; Issigonis did not fight against these properties, but he had never set out to provide them.

When they were announced, the Minis offered remarkable value—and BMC immediately provided themselves with a cross which had to be borne for many years to come. The car was so cheap that it was only barely profitable, and not even a great flood of sales could alter that. It was out of the early career of the Mini that the famous industry aphorism: 'Mini-car, mini-profits', was born.

In 1959, when the motoring public first saw the Minis, the 'basic' models cost £497, whereas the de Luxe models cost £537: the difference included a built-in heater, opening rear quarter windows and one or two other details. In truth, these prices were cut to the bone, for the Morris Minor sold for £590, the new Ford Anglia for £589 and the troublesome, but technically interesting, Triumph Herald for a whopping £702. Only the ancient 1930-type Ford Popular undercut the Mini, at £419, and this was just about to disappear from the scene. The Minis could certainly have been priced a little higher, without harming their prospects, without hitting the Morris Minor 1000 too hard, and with great benefit to profitability.

In the beginning, although the press loved the cars, the buying customers were not as impressed. Perhaps they did not trust the idea of front-wheel-drive from a company which had always been wedded to building strictly conventional, not to say boring, models. Perhaps they did not like the tiny aspect of the car. Perhaps, even, they could not really believe their eyes. Was it, however, that most of them agreed with the Duke of Cambridge who once said that: 'All change, at any time and for any purpose, is utterly to be deprecated'?.

Soon, however, word began to get around. I bought my own Mini in March 1960, six months after launch, never having driven one, and being influenced purely by rave reports by friends and colleagues who had been more fortunate. If you could accept the teething troubles and the minor annoyances (which most people did), it was very easy to fall in love with a Mini. Only 19,749 Minis were built in 1959 (at Cowley and Longbridge), but that figure rose to 116,677 in 1960, 157,059 in 1961 and rocketed to 216,087 in 1962. By that time the Cooper-Minis were on sale, as were the vans, the estate cars, the Riley Elf and the Wolseley Hornet versions—and there seemed to be a Mini for every occasion.

Perhaps if the Mini had arrived a few years earlier *or* a few years later, it might not have succeeded in the way that it did. As it happened, the car, its character, and its behaviour, were all absolutely right for the period. Britain's economy was booming, prosperity seemed to be everywhere and most people were confident about their future. It was the 'Never had it so good' period (as Prime Minister Harold MacMillan had told us), when the world seemed to be at peace, when there were exciting technological innovations at all sides, when gloom and despondency had been banished. The fuel crisis inspired by the Suez war of 1956 was forgotten and buried in the national conscience. Fathers had even toned down admonitory remarks like, 'You don't think we fought the last war for you kids to do that, do you?', and young people were about to start asserting themselves. The 1960s—the Swinging 60s if only we had known it—were just around the corner.

Nothing could have been more appropriate to the period than the Mini. It was right for the world's rapidly worsening traffic jams and crowded city streets, it was a

Definitive Mini—the 1959 Morris Mini-Minor, as revealed in August 1959.

Left *The Mini was astonishingly space-efficient—a feature improved upon by the Metro in 1980.* **Above** *In 1959, the Mini was all about marginal motoring, and costs had to be kept down. There was nothing stylish in the facia layout.*

good substitute for sports car motoring for the young who couldn't afford to insure one, and it seemed to be completely classless as a machine for all types to use. Alec Issigonis' 'working-class car for working-class people' faded away almost overnight. The Mini, whether he liked it or not, was a car for the trendies.

It was the start of the Mini Phenomenon. It was a car which the nation, and the media, took to its heart and whose name speedily passed into general usage. Just as the BBC were no longer able to call a Land-Rover anything but a Land-Rover, a Mini was soon just that. As far as the BMC marketing staffs were concerned, the Austin and Morris badges might just as well have been dropped altogether.

People started customising Minis and a whole new cottage industry grew up to supply bits and pieces. Seats, steering wheels, oil coolers, 'nerfing bars' (extra bumpers), even boot extensions, were all put on offer and thousands were sold. BMC's marketing managers, who were in love with the whole idea of 'badge-engineering', and were out to squeeze every possible sale from the market, got in on the act themselves. By the mid-1960s they had encouraged the birth of Super de Luxe Minis, Riley and Wolseley versions, Mini-Cooper, estate cars (some with wood trim in Olde Worlde Cottage style, some without), vans and pick-ups. The very specialised Mini-Cooper S had arrived to take the sporting world by storm and that most extraordinary Mini of all, the Mini-Moke, looked like a rugged little cross-country vehicle, even though it was still only equipped with front-wheel-drive and

tiny wheels. Minis with two engines (one at the front, one at the rear) were built—
John Cooper almost killed himself in one—and all manner of special-bodied versions
began to appear.

BMC themselves encouraged the building of a 'beach Mini', without doors or
weather protection, racing drivers smoothed off their Minis by removing all the
outside hinges and welded flanges, one firm built a smart mid-engined sports car with
the Mini engine/transmission power pack behind the driver, and a whole variety of
special body styles were erected on the Mini's basic floor pan and running gear.
There were standard-bodied Minis with superbly modified and equipped interiors,
Minis with hatchbacks (which pre-dated the ADO88 by ten years), convertible
Minis, Ogle Minis, and even tiny articulated-trailer Minis.

More than that, there was the cheeky and quite unsinkable character of the Mini
which automatically seemed to rub off on its owners. They were quick, adept at
slipping in and out of heavy traffic, and incredibly nimble. With the aid of specialist
attention, the faster Coopers and Cooper Ss could become extremely rapid indeed.
One popular, if anti-social, rear-window sticker of the period proudly proclaimed to
the reader that: 'You have just been Mini'd'. Perhaps that famous *Motor* cartoonist,
Brockbank, summed it up best of all. The choleric owner of a large Jaguar had just
been passed at high speed by a Mini, and was spluttering to his wife: 'If the good Lord
had meant cars that size to do 100 mph, He'd have given them larger wheels!'.

By this time BMC had allowed themselves thoroughly to be caught up in the
romance of Mini-making, and the Mini's character. Reality, however, would one day
have to set in. One day, somehow, the Mini would have to be replaced.

Chapter 2

Replacing the Mini
The false starts

At first, the Mini's problem, if there *was* a problem, was that it was too successful too easily. It sold so well, looked so good, and made so many headlines without trying, that BMC's management grew complacent. The millionth Mini was built in 1965, and by that time annual production was reaching towards the quarter million mark. Why, then, should anyone—engineer, salesman, or director—worry about its replacement? As yet, for sure, it had no obvious competition. Perhaps, like the VW Beetle, it could go on indefinitely? It was easy enough for the Mini's future to be ignored for the moment, for BMC's management had far more important things to worry about.

The corporation had entered the 1960s in a positive blur of activity, and spent the next few years adding to the confusion. Not only were they busily adding to their range of products, and announcing as many derivatives as they could think of, and building new factories, but they had also set about the prestigious business of expansion by takeover. Sir Leonard Lord, his health gradually wilting after a lifetime's high-pressure top-managment work, began to plan the succession in 1956, when he made George Harriman his deputy. In 1961 he handed over the chair to 'Young George', who became Sir George in 1965. It was under Sir George's direction that BMC, which was really big enough in all truth, got bigger and bigger as the 1960s progressed. In 1965 it secured its future body supplies by taking over the Pressed Steel Co of Cowley, and in 1966 it completed a real ego-trip by merging with Sir William Lyons' Jaguar group. The resulting monolith, British Motor Holdings, existed for less than two years before it, in turn, merged with Sir Donald Stokes' Leyland Group at the beginning of 1968.

If you are already confused by such corporate manoeuvrings, please don't feel inadequate for, at the time, so was almost everyone else. The new colossus, called British Leyland, not only commanded the largest market share in the car industry (41 per cent in 1968), but it also inherited an enormously diverse, and illogically arranged, line-up of cars. When the merger was announced Britain's foremost motoring magazine, *Autocar*, produced a complete list of the cars in production. Not only were there 37 different types, but they varied from the tiny Mini itself to the vast and patrician Daimler limousines, and from the delicacies of the 150 mph Jaguar E-Type sports car to the all-purpose four-wheel-drive Land-Rover. It was clear to any thoughtful economist or product planner that there was big scope for immediate rationalisation, but it is now well-known that this task was not tackled until it was too late.

But that wasn't all. Even at 'The Austin'—the name always given to the Longbridge complex by its workforce, and by Birmingham people—there had been great changes in the 1960s. Not only had many new models been introduced, but the factory buildings had been expanded mightily to help build them.

By the mid-1960s, the Longbridge site had almost completely been built over. The redundant 2½-acre factory, which Herbert Austin had bought in 1905, had been dwarfed by new buildings within a generation and by this time it had almost disappeared from view. The first big body-building factory, West Works, had been erected at the other side of the main Birmingham-Bristol road, and the North Works (on the other side of the branch railway line) had joined it. During the Second World War, not only had a large area of land south of the factory buildings been used as an aerodrome, but a massive 'shadow factory' building had been erected at Cofton Hackett, just a short distance away from it.

The huge expansion master-minded by Sir Leonard Lord occupied the 1950s and 1960s, when two enormous assembly buildings were laid out on the aerodrome, in a commanding position on top of the hill. Car Assembly Building (CAB) No 1 was completed in 1951, ready for the A30 to go into production, and was linked to the rest of the works by a series of tunnels and conveyors, while CAB2 finally came on stream in 1962. Longbridge's ability to build cars rose dramatically in this period, from less than 3,000 cars a week in 1950 to no less than 10,000 cars a week in 1963. Mini sales, need it be said, were booming, with 5,000 cars a week leaving Longbridge and Cowley.

Alec Issigonis' success with the Mini brought him speedy recognition, and a great deal more influence on future policy. Even before the Mini was safely launched, he was looking ahead to the next model, the larger and more complex Austin/Morris 1100, and soon after that he started to develop the even larger 1800 front-wheel-drive cars. From being Sir Leonard Lord's own personal designer/genius in 1956, Issigonis became BMC's chief engineer in 1957, and its technical director in 1961.

George Harriman, having tasted the success of the Mini, and having seen all the promise of ADO16, the Austin/Morris 1100, seemed to decide that BMC's way to fame was to concentrate on advanced engineering. Gradually, as the decade progressed, the conventional, but profitable, saloons like A40 Farinas and the larger A60s and A110s began to slip out of the limelight, while very little was done to revive the 'Morris' name except to slap it on to the front of any new car which Issigonis and the Longbridge-based designers produced. 'Creative engineering' became fashionable and even appeared in the adverts.

BMC, therefore, was really far too busy, and far too absorbed in this new expansionary phase, to start preparing for a new Mini. The 1100 came along in 1962 and sold even better than the Mini had done at first. Two years later there was the 1800—a 'misjudgement' according to some observers, Plain Jane according to others, but enormously practical according to all its owners. By this time, indeed, Alec Issigonis had risen far above the ranks of a mere engineer, and was being treated by some journalists as something of a guru or soothsayer. What he said, rather than what he did, became newsworthy. When Issigonis suggested that, 'Drivers should be uncomfortable, so that they stay alert', some people forgave the terrible seats in the Minis, and when he suggested that the next generation of small cars would shrink even further so that the driver might have to stand up, he was taken quite seriously. He was a believer in tiny engines which revved furiously, and no one sought to dissuade him.

The problem was that while his theories, and his layouts, worked very well indeed on small cars, they worked less and less well on the larger cars which followed. Further, he had a much-publicised dislike of styling for its own sake, and the consequence was that the 1800 and, later, the Maxi, all needed a good deal of brightening up before the public found them acceptable. Even so, when Issigonis left the design of new cars to his subordinates, the results were even more disappointing— no one, surely, now has many good things to say about the ponderous Austin 3-litre of 1967, or of the Rolls-Royce engined Vanden Plas Princess R which preceded it?

It was this sort of process which led a financially and functionally weakened BMC/BMH to merge with Sir Donald Stokes' aggressively-managed Leyland Group at the beginning of 1968, and one which unerringly led to further financial disasters in the next few years. By producing the Mini, 110/1300, and 1800 in the last few years, BMC's creative genius appeared to have exhausted itself. When Sir Donald Stokes moved Issigonis smartly sideways in the spring of 1968, and installed Harry Webster from Triumph in his place, he was appalled to find that apart from the ADO14 (Austin Maxi) project, which was running late, was still in development problems, and which looked plain ugly, there was only the long-nose Mini Clubman facelift on the way, after which the cupboard was bare. Longbridge's design strength was quite clearly over-stretched. Years after he had had time to establish himself at Longbridge, Harry Webster once told me that the company was short of designers, and short of control; his job, he reasoned, was to do something about it.

Not that the Mini was ever neglected by its designers for lack of interest, merely because they could never find the time. If management was not interested in seeing a replacement Mini produced, busy subordinates of Alec Issigonis like Charles Griffin were not inclined to harm the prospects of something which was a firm project by going off into a corner and playing with big changes to the Mini. It was still a time, incidentally, when engineers *could* play around without being hampered by product planners, or by new legislation. Until the end of the 1960s, the only major changes made to the Mini were that Hydrolastic suspension units, connected front to rear, replaced rubber suspension on the saloons for 1965 (the change was reversed in 1969, by the way), that the car became a 'Mk II' in 1967, with a 1-litre engine option, and that an all-synchromesh gearbox was phased in during 1968. In the meantime Lockheed's ingenious four-speed automatic transmission had become optional, and the tuned-up Coopers and Cooper Ss had become very popular. Nothing, however, had ever been done about the styling, or about the seating layout, and the arrival of the long-nose Clubman of 1969 was really an irrelevance.

The rest of the world, however, had already started to show appreciation of the Mini by copying its layout. The use of a transversely-mounted four-cylinder water-cooled engine, with its transmission mounted underneath it, was far too fundamental an installation ever to be patented, and Alex Issigonis was flattered, rather than irritated, by the competition which eventually appeared.

It all took time for, as BMC had discovered, such investment in radically new layouts was not easily authorised. Chronologically, the first two 'copies', if that is the right word, were by Alec Issigonis himself—the Morris 1100 of 1962 and the Austin 1800 of 1964—but after that the competition arrived, thick and fast. Fiat, operating through their Autobianchi subsidiary, produced the Primula in 1964, and Peugeot announced the 204 in 1965. Soon after that there was the air-cooled Honda 1300, and after it, the Simca 1100. It was all, however, merely a prelude. The truly Big Battalions—Ford, General Motors, Renault and VW—all hung back, and watched the rest of the world; they were not convinced that the world's motorists wanted to buy cars as small as the Mini, and were not experienced in building them.

It was Fiat which was first to make its move, with the launch of the 1.1-litre 128 in 1969, and the same firm followed up with the smaller, but even more important, 127 a couple of years later. When Renault chimed in, for 1972, with its eye-catching R5 model, the product planners of the world sat up and took notice. Before then, there had been proper Minis, like *the* Mini, and there had been larger cars, like the BMC 1100 and the Peugeot 204. Suddenly, the Fiat 127 and the Renault 5 had invented a new category—the age of the Supermini had begun.

But BMC engineers did not need to wake up to the challenge of 1972 from blissful oblivion, for those hard-working people who had managed to find some time, on occasion, had been nursing their ambitions for some years. There might not have been a formal Product Planning department (not under Sir George Harriman, nor yet under Lord Stokes and his staff), but there were still designers, enthusiasts even, who liked to look ahead and identify the future challenge. Charles Griffin and Harry Webster encouraged this, and added their own six-penn'orth from time to time. Everyone had ideas. Fred Coultas, the engineer who did so much to guide the development of the Metro from its earliest days, right through to becoming the BL success-story of the 1980s, once commented: 'Some of us have been trying to replace the Mini since about 1964'.

There had been other small-car designs for BMC even before there was a real Mini. Sir Leonard Lord might have been an abrupt, laconic, engineer's engineer, but he was not a fool. Well before the Suez crisis shocked the British motor industry into life, he realised that better, and technically more advanced, models would soon be needed.

Sir Leonard was a great believer in creating corporate unrest. Nothing made him more gleeful than setting Austin against Morris in the battle for sales (BMC would gain, he thought, because both teams would try harder than ever). He liked to surprise his engineers by telling them he had asked another section, or outside consultants, to do the same job for him. He was a complete workaholic and a compulsive meddler. He was manager, salesman, engineer and stylist.

So it was in 1956 that he set up another of his informal design competitions. While Alec Issigonis was setting up his staff at Longbridge, Sir Leonard also commissioned ERA of Dunstable to design an advanced car for him. In the beginning, ERA had built a series of famous racing cars, but after the Second World War they had been bought by racing driver/businessman, Leslie Johnson, and offered consultancy services to the motor industry. By 1956, Johnson was dead, but ERA were more active than ever.

It was one of those projects which never really stood a chance of acceptance, for ERA was guided by Laurence Pomeroy, technical editor of *Motor*, whose writings were flowery and well-regarded, if sometimes suspect, whose leanings were towards advanced rather than proven engineering ideas, and who had no established track-record in design. Would it be unkind to revive that famous aphorism: 'Those who can, do. Those who can't, teach?'

Pomeroy's ideas, and designer David Hodkin's practical talents, went towards the design of a new car in complete secrecy. Pomeroy, who had known Issigonis for many years, was not actually forbidden to speak to him ever again, but was most firmly told not to discuss the project with him. Issigonis knew that opposition had been set up at Dunstable, but did not know what they were hatching.

The ERA project was more adventurous than anything Issigonis had ever attempted until then. The engine and transmission were to be at the rear, mounted transversely across the tail, and drove the rear wheels. Most of the major castings were to be in light-alloy, produced from pressure dies, which promised to be a very costly way of building them.

Innovation did not end there. Pomeroy and Hodkin proposed an ingenious method of gear changing, which retained a conventional gearbox, but involved changes of ratio at fixed engine speeds. Naturally there was to be all-independent suspension, but instead of conventional steel springs Pomeroy suggested the use of Firestone air suspension bags. One big advantage of the general layout was that it proved possible to provide luggage lockers at the front *and* at the rear (behind the engine/ transmission).

In retrospect, it never stood a chance of being accepted, and ERA, Hodkin and the unfortunate Pomeroy must have been misguided to think that it would. In Pomeroy's own words, 'This design was too ambitious, the time taken to get two cars running too long, and the experience of the team on practical production details too small'. The 'Maximin', as it became known, was eventually delivered to Longbridge, speedily dismissed from contention by the decisive Sir Leonard Lord, and stowed away in one of the redundant air-raid tunnels which are burrowed under the surface of the site. No trace of this project now remains.

Charles Griffin, an ex-Wolseley Motors man, and therefore still not quite a died-in-the-wool 'Austin' man, was also encouraged to devise a minimum-cost car at Cowley, with ex-Nuffield designers and development engineers. His solution was to use a rough-and-ready two-cylinder version of the ubiquitous BMC A-Series engine, transversely mounted across the car ahead of the rear wheels (and driving the rear wheels). The body style, which was never properly developed, would have been on the 'large-bubble' layout, rather like that employed by Fiat with the Multipla estate car (DO19, as it was coded), would have had wheels even smaller than those of the Mini became (and that small size was controversial enough!), but it placed the front seat passengers very far forward, just as they were positioned in the new wave of 'bubble' cars. As a cost-minimising exercise it worked, but in almost every other respect it was a failure. The only prototype was never even finished.

In the first half of the 1960s, while BMC engineers were fully occupied with the development of the 110s and 1800s, plus the permutations of badging, engine size change, transmission and suspension modification, they had little time, or inclination, to think about a new Mini model. In the cramped styling department out at the back of Austin's 1940s executive office building (known to all and sundry, including its occupants, as the 'Kremlin'), Dick Burzi's staff were fully occupied not only with brand new cars like the Maxi and the Austin 3-litre, but with wider Minis, barrel-shaped Minis, longer-wheelbase four-door Minis, and coupé (MG Midget-intended) Minis. All had the same basic floor pan, suspension and engine/transmission layouts.

By 1967, however, Alec Issigonis had cleared the decks somewhat. The 1100/1300 models were in full flower, with no fewer than six badges and grilles on the same basic body, while the 1800s now included Austin, Morris and Wolseley versions; and Riley and Vanden Plas derivatives had also been mocked-up. The fourth generation of BMC front-wheel-drive car, the ADO14 Maxi, had at last been cleared for production. The rear-drive Austin 3-litre, the ADO61, had really been little to do with him, but had been controlled by Charles Griffin.

At this point, Issigonis, trading on his unique reputation within BMC, made a remarkable request to BMC's chairman, Sir George Harriman. 'Please relieve me of all my normal responsibilities for BMC engineering', he said, 'I want to design a new Mini.' Charles Griffin, he thought, could cope with day-to-day matters. For the next year or so, he wanted to immerse himself in a proper Mini replacement study.

Sir George agreed. At the beginning of 1968 Issigonis retired to a quiet corner of Longbridge and with six carefully selected assistants (some of whom had gone through the same process with him on the original Mini, in 1957), he set to work. The new car really would be new—new style, new suspensions, new engine and transmission. If approved, a massive investment would be required. Its name was 9X, and as far as I can see it never even acquired a conventional BMC ADO number.

It would not have been Issigonis if the car had not flown against known trends. The latest European 'copycat' Minis were getting bigger, and more complex, but Issigonis was having none of this. 9X would be smaller, not larger, simpler rather than more complicated. The car his designers produced was four inches shorter than the existing Mini, at 9 feet 8 inches, but it had rather more leg room. The engine/transmission unit, transversely mounted but entirely new, was to weigh only 200 lb compared with the 340 lb of the existing Mini. There was to be a semi-hatchback, to be sure, but only two passenger doors. As to ornamentation, Issigonis didn't believe in that sort of thing, so front and rear overhang was minimal, even less that that of the current Mini itself.

The style was by Burzi's department this time, and was crisp, simple, and attractive. The exposed welded seams of the Mini had been banished, though the general two-box layout had been retained. Corners had been squared off, rather than rounded away, and the 'wheel-at-each-corner' look was ensured by the use of existing 10 inch Mini wheels, and the tiny overhang: the wheelbase of 9X was the same as before, 6 feet 8 inches.

It was under the skin, however, where all the innovations were made. Even though Sir George Harriman and his board would not give him a definite commitment to future production, and the development budget was tiny, Issigonis pushed ahead with an all-new chassis. Out went the old A-Series engine, and out went the Hydrolastic suspension units.

In their place, the team, led by John Sheppard, produced a new engine, new transmission, and new suspension systems. The new engine—one of many with which BMC/BL were to dabble in the next few years—was a compact little four-cylinder unit, meant to be built in various sizes between 750 cc and 1,000 cc, and it had a single overhead camshaft driven from the crankshaft by a cogged belt. In engineering terms, it was something of a 'sandwich' design, for the head, the crankcase and the sump were all to be in aluminium alloy, but the cylinder block itself was cast iron. To keep the engine narrow for its transverse location, if not short, the oil pump was mounted at the nose of the crankshaft (ie, at the side of the engine as it was installed in the car), while the electrical alternator was built in to the flywheel at the other end of the engine.

To match this delicate little unit, which produced up to 60 bhp for a one litre engine (astonishingly better than the 38 bhp of the 1-litre Mk II Mini), there was a new two-shaft gearbox, beneath and behind the engine as it was already placed in the Minis, but much more simple, and much less likely to produce a lot of noise.

The suspension not only relied on steel springs for the very first time on any BMC mini-car, but the Hydrolastic principle of inter-connection between front and rear

Above *The first serious attempt to replace the Mini was Alec Issigonis' 9X project in 1968. Like the Mini, it had front-wheel-drive, but the transverse engine was all new, and normal steel springs were used in the suspension.* **Below** *Even in 1968, 9X had a hatchback, though it did not go all the way down to bumper level.*

The only Minis with opening rear doors were the successful little estate cars, which shared their floor pan, and many panels, with the Mini van. There was to be no estate car scheme in the ADO88/LC8 plans.

was also abandoned. In its place, Issigonis' team provided conventional MacPherson struts and coil springs (like those used by Ford) at the front, and trailing arms and transverse torsion bars (like the Renault 16) at the rear. This set-up was cheaper, no less compact, and considerably softer than that being built into all Minis at the time. The whole car, indeed, was designed with an eye to simplicity and low cost—figures now disclosed claim that there would have been 42 per cent fewer separate components than in an existing Mini. It was Issigonis' last overall design for Longbridge and it was cancelled very soon after the first car was finished. So what went wrong?

Its demise could not be blamed on design deficiencies but on commercial manoeuvrings. Even while 9X was being designed, BMC were on the way to losing their independence. Talks with the Leyland Group had begun in 1964, on a very tentative basis, but took on some urgency in 1967 when the British government (with Prime Minister Harold Wilson and the Minister of Technology, Anthony Wedgwood-Benn, acting as brokers and marriage makers) encouraged Sir Donald Stokes, Leyland's chairman, and Sir George Harriman to discuss a merger. Events moved steadily in favour of Leyland, and a takeover bid, rather than an agreed merger, for BMC's profits were fading away while Leyland's were rising, and BMC's UK market share was also slipping back towards that of Ford.

Matters came to a head in the January of 1968, and what was publicly presented was a merger with everyone's consent. Within weeks, however, it became clear that Leyland, and Sir Donald Stokes, would be dominant in the new group, to be called the British Leyland Motor Corporation. Leyland managers moved into Longbridge right away, where, among other things, they discovered from a cost analysis that the Mini was only making a £15 profit on each car sold, a miserable and quite unacceptable contribution.

In April 1968, Stokes drafted George Turnbull and Harry Webster into Longbridge from Triumph, Turnbull to run the plant and Harry Webster to knock some practical sense into the design and development function. Webster spent the first few months of his time at Longbridge, 'rushing round, turning off all the expenditure

A late 1970s Mini, showing the wind-up door windows and the concealed door hinges introduced later in its life. It was still a wonderfully compact layout, on which Metro would have to improve.

taps. Money was rushing out of Longbridge, and we had nothing to show for it—it was quite terrifying'.

He also got down to a different new-model programme which Sir Donald deemed necessary. The ADO14 (Maxi) project was hastily upgraded to make it commercially acceptable (Stokes thought the car's interior ridiculously stark—'Like a hen-coop'— and no one had a good word to say for the cable gearchange), while all efforts were directed to the immediate design of a new conventional car. In the end, therefore, 9X perished not because it was a bad car, but because it came along at the wrong time. Stokes wanted a Cortina-beater—BMC *needed* a Cortina-beater—and the ADO28 Marina project was it.

From this moment, Issigonis seemed to lose heart and never again influenced overall design of BMC (now BL) cars. British Leyland made him their research chief and he was deservedly knighted in 1969. For years his steam cars, his new automatic transmissions and his other bright ideas were regularly fed back into the design offices for consideration, but none have yet been taken up on production cars. After reaching his 65th birthday at the end of 1971 he elected to go into semi-retirement, as an Advanced Design Consultant to British Leyland and, for a memento of this occasion, he asked for, and was presented with, a No 10 Meccano set, complete with steam-producer and electric power unit! *Autocar*, perhaps, was being unusually prophetic of names when it headlined the news: 'Mighty Mini maestro retires'. By the time the definitive Metro was on the way, Sir Alec Issigonis had virtually disappeared from the Longbridge scene.

For the next few years, all thoughts of replacement Minis were forgotten. The existing car, still being built at the rate of 250,000 to 300,000 examples a year, was rationalised, changed, but little improved. The high-performance Coopers gradually faded away, while the long-nose Clubman and 1275GT models arrived. Before the end of the 1960s the 'Austin' and 'Morris' badges had been swept away, and 'Mini' took their place. The public had got their way at last, even if it took years for the British vehicle licencing authorities to be convinced! Wind-up windows arrived at last (years after the accessory trade had first put them on the market), and from time to time there were trim and equipment improvements.

When Leyland merged with BMC, many proud and fine words had been spoken, but as the years progressed, these faded away. The workforce in the group often downed tools on the flimsiest of excuses and the Corporation's share of the market began to melt away. The fact that the much-vaunted 'Cortina-beater', the Morris Marina, proved to be nothing of the kind, and that the front-drive Austin Allegro, which began to replace the 1100/1300 models in 1973, was not a great success, didn't help. TV comics, as cruel as ever, loved it, and the sad jokes proliferated:

'Rich father, boasting in the golf club: ''My son asked me to buy him a cowboy outfit last Christmas, so I gave him British Leyland''.'

'Doctor to patient: ''You're run down, and you need a good rest. Why don't you change your job? Go and work for British Leyland''.'

It was all very sad. The workforce were bewildered, not well informed, and led by aggressive and bloody-minded shop stewards. Lord Stokes, who knew a potential profit when he saw one, preached the constant litany that British Leyland's future was assured if only the cars could be built to the right standard, in enough quantity.

Dedicated staff, however, never lost hope. By 1972, when Lord Stokes, John Barber and George Turnbull decided that the existing Mini was not a car with which to face the 1980s, a complete analysis of the market place, and its trends, had taken place. Three paper projects were being studied:

Code-name Ant was about the same size as Mini, but had a lot more luggage space and a choice of 750 cc or 950 cc engines. It would have had the alternative of two-door or three-door (hatchback) styles.

Ladybird was between 15 and 20 inches longer than Mini, between 2.5 and 4.5 inches wider, and with a much more roomy interior package. It would have 900 cc

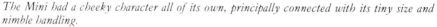

The Mini had a cheeky character all of its own, principally connected with its tiny size and nimble handling.

or 1,100 cc engines and be specifically a three-door hatchback to fight the Fiat 127/Renault 5 concept head on.

Dragonfly was the largest of the three, 24 to 30 inches longer than Mini (as large, therefore, as the Allegro, which was still on the secret list), and even wider than Ladybird. It would have had engines of 1,000 cc or 1,200 cc and conventional three-box (booted) styling. In many ways this was something of a successor to the Marina, and would have been competing against the rear-wheel-drive Ford Escorts and Vauxhall Vivas and against the Fiat 128s and Simca 1100s.

A lot of thought went into the choice between these three projects, but Dragonfly was soon eliminated, and full-size clay models were then shaped of the 10 foot long, 86 inch wheelbase Ant and the 11 foot 6 inch long, 90 inch wheelbase Ladybird. Most of the styling work was carried out at Longbridge, though Harry Webster also invited his old Triumph consultant, Giovanni Michelotti from Turin, to provide a clay for the Ladybird concept.

Styling functions inside British Leyland had only recently been rationalised for, when the merger took place, the long-established styling house at Longbridge was operating in parallel with a new office at Cowley, where Roy Haynes had been attracted over to BMC (from Ford) by Joe Edwards, who was Sir George Harriman's managing director. One of Haynes' most able lieutenants at Cowley, who followed his boss from Essex to Oxfordshire, was Harris Mann.

'We did the ADO28—the Marina—down at Cowley', Mann told me, 'but when Harry Webster took charge he wanted to see all styling work concentrated at Longbridge, so in the middle of doing the Allegro—that would be 1970/1971—we moved up to Longbridge. There was not much spare cash at the time, so we had to be

Much ado about . . . nothing? The only major restyle, in a generation, was to make the long-nose 'Clubman' style out of the original car. But there was no increase in the wheelbase, or interior space. The 'run-flat' Dunlop Denovo tyres on this model were an innovation.

No hatchback on the Mini, even after 20 years—though specialist coachbuilders could produce such styles if asked.

housed in the big building known as the ''Elephant House'', not far from the Kremlin.'

It is a lofty structure, almost entirely walled in plate glass, but it had not been designed as a styling studio. Way back in the expansionary days of Sir Leonard Lord and George Harriman, it had been built as a commercial vehicle showroom, but had been empty for some time. To a layman it looks ideal as a styling house, because of all that glass, but Rex Fleming (who ran the place for Tom Penny through the entire Mini-replacement/Metro programme) and Harris Mann don't find that so. 'The problem', Rex said, 'is that the sun rises over *here* (pointing to the east) and sets over *there* (to the west), and naturally takes all day to move across. The lighting emphasis on our clays is altering, minute by minute. In an ideal world, we'd like a bigger building with no natural light at all, but row after row of diffused, artificial light. And, of course, a safe and secure outside viewing area, which we don't have at all.'

Roy Haynes never made the move from Cowley to Longbridge, but left to set up his own design business and it was Harris Mann who began to have more and more say in the exterior shape of things, now that the long-serving BMC stylist, Dick Burzi, had retired. Mann had shaped the Allegro, which was controversial, the TR7 (even more so), and had also tackled the wedge-style Austin-Morris Princess which was well-liked by almost everyone.

Once a great deal of information gathered by marked research departments had been collated, not only from British motorists, but from those in Western Europe as well, the demise of the Dragonfly was soon followed by loss of confidence in the Ant. Perhaps the name—Ant—told its own story, for the car quite literally seemed to be too small. Original buyers of the Mini were now tending to look for rather larger cars. The Mini was still selling enormously well considering that it was already an elderly design (318,000 built in 1971, 307,000 in 1972—in spite of repeated strikes and other disruptions at Cowley and Longbridge)—but it was felt that it would be unwise to replace it without making a larger car available instead. Ant and Ladybird both developed under the ADO74 code, but it was Ladybird, the larger version of ADO74, which was chosen for further development.

The barrel-sided Mini, as mocked up by the styling department in the early 1970s, was not enough of an advance on the Mini itself.

By this time, and in spite of the fact that British Leyland's profits were still see-sawing all over the place (£39 million in 1968, £4 million in 1970, £32 million in 1971, and more promised in 1972), management was getting quite excited about the idea of a new small car. It was going to be larger than the Mini, smaller than the Allegro and—hopefully—more successful than either of them.

Even so, ADO74 attracted a great deal of conflict. The marketing staffs wanted it rather larger because that was the sort of 'Supermini' which was beginning to sell in huge numbers, while the financial staff wanted it larger so that it could earn bigger profits for them. Leyland International, on the other hand, were not as sure, because they wanted something different to sell, rather than something similar to sell. Lord Stokes was still a great believer in the niche-filling approach to building cars, and LI agreed with him.

ADO74, however, soon crystallised around a 7 foot 6 inch (90 inch) wheelbase and attractive, rounded, styling by Harris Mann in the now-classic two-box, three-door, layout. It was 11 feet 6 inches long and 5 feet 1.5 inches wide (whereas the Mini was 10 feet long and 4 feet 7.5 inches wide) and, if built, it would probably have carried forward Sir Alex Issigonis' 9X suspension philosophy of steel springs, by MacPherson strut at the front, and by torsion bars at the rear. Early sketches and 'package' layouts show the fuel tank under the boot floor (rather than in the boot, on the right, as in Mini and 9X). The wedge nose which became so familiar on the 1975 Princess and the Metro itself was much in evidence, while the wheels (though not finalised) would definitely have been much larger than those used on the Mini, with 12 inch or even 13 inch Allegro-type rims.

Technically, much of interest was in the proposed engine/transmission assembly, which might have been all-new. In the spring of 1972, when styling work was just starting, Austin-Morris began project work on the K-Series engine, a single-overhead camshaft unit which would have had its four-speed or five-speed gearbox and final drive assemblies all in the same lower casting, which could have been in cast iron or light alloy. The cooling radiator, incidentally, would have been at the front—

the location already finalised for the new Allegro, and the forthcoming wedge-style Princess.

Politics, however, got in the way of engineering and ADO74 soon began to languish under a sea of changes and reorganisations. It did not officially die until the end of 1973, but its future had been shot away long before then.

It all started in the euphoria of early 1973, when Lord Stokes announced a £500 million expansion programme for British Leyland, aimed at lifting total production from the 1.1 million achieved in 1972 to a potential of 1.5 millions. Not only did this plan talk about new models, and new engines, but it also mentioned the need to build an entirely new factory on an unspecified new 'greenfield' site. Lord Stokes said that: 'This is the beginning of a very exciting era for British Leyland and I think our designers, engineers and production men are going to provide you with a British motor industry of which you will be very proud'.

These were brave words, bravely spoken. But Lord Stokes had not finished yet. He also announced that British Leyland would shortly be taking over the 14-storey Burmah-Castrol House, in London's Marylebone Road, and that he had decided—prematurely, as it transpired—on the management succession when he should decide to retire at 65 years of age. He revealed that henceforth he would not be operating as the group's managing director, but merely as chairman. By appointing John Barber as his 'right-hand man', as deputy chairman and deputy chief executive, and by making George Turnbull managing director, but responsible to Barber, he set off a real power struggle, which was not to come to a head for several months, and which was to make waves down through the hierarchy.

Turnbull had been Stokes' protégé at Coventry in the 1960s, and was a production specialist who had been trying to make sense of Austin-Morris since 1968, whereas John Barber was the finance man, ex-AEI and ex-Ford Motor Co, who had joined Stokes in London before the merger took place. Each had expected to be nominated as the 'Number Two' and clearly Turnbull was very disappointed.

Barber's influence on ADO74 was immediate. Personally he thought the car had grown too large and that he would rather see a direct replacement for Mini. But not yet. In any case he thought the amount of investment finance likely to be required (£130 million was mentioned at the beginning of 1974) was too high and that he would rather see this much spent on larger and more profitable models. This, by the way, was a decision taken just as the impact of the 1973 Yom Kippur war, and the speedy quadrupling of crude oil prices, took place. It was a decision quite breathtaking for its error, and it was to put back British Leyland's mini-car philosophy by four years at least.

The power struggle lasted for a mere four months, when George Turnbull abruptly resigned, and John Barber took over the title of managing director as well as that of deputy chairman. Turnbull soon went off to set up the Hyundai Pony project in South Korea, made a success of it, then spent some time running the Iran National car-making project (which assembled Hillman Hunters from Coventry-made components) and eventually came back to Britain as chairman of the Talbot company, which had been Chrysler UK before the Peugeot-Citroën group had taken it over in 1978. The Power Game? You bet!

But that wasn't all. Managing director of Austin-Morris (which became a 'Product Division, responsible for planning, designing and marketing its own product') became Dick Perry, a mere stripling of 43 years of age, and there was a general reshuffle of jobs at this level throughout the Corporation.

In 1973/1974, the ADO74 project came close to being adopted as the 'official' Supermini design. It was aerodynamically smooth, but rather too large for some management tastes. It never progressed beyond the mock-up stage.

From this point, with inflation worsening, the energy crisis deepening, and with industrial unrest at its height in the midst of the 1974 miners' strike (and the 'three-day-week' which followed), British Leyland's fortunes went rapidly downhill, even though their market share held up remarkably well. During 1974 Austin-Morris' profitability disappeared altogether and, as if morale was not bad enough already, sales director, Filmer Paradise, walked out and Harry Webster moved on to become technical director of the Automotive Products group. Observers saw this as the end of ex-Triumph men's domination of Austin-Morris, but they were not all sure what it meant for the future.

Chapter 3

Under new management
Ryder, Leyland Cars, ADO88

British Leyland's financial collapse at the end of 1974 was sudden, serious and traumatic. Most observers knew that the corporation was not at all healthy and that there were personality problems at the top. Its public image was in disarray, but few realised just how serious the situation was. The City of London, and its Stock Market, however, had their own very accurate ideas. A rights issue, of shares and convertible loan stock, flopped miserably, and the group began to look dangerously short of cash. Even so, Lord Stokes never lost his buoyancy in public, saying at one time that, when all the big plants were working normally, the profits they made were almost embarrassingly high.

It might have been wishful thinking, but it looked, and sounded, quite convincing.

At the sketching stage, concepts are sometimes very dramatic. This Mini-type of car was drawn in January 1974.

Two ways of developing a Mini-replacement concept in the 1974-1975 period. This car had rather sculptured lines . . .

Accordingly, when Anthony Wedgwood-Benn, the Labour government's Minister for Trade and Industry, made a shock statement to the House of Commons just before Christmas 1974, that British Leyland was short of money and that it (the government) was willing to underwrite the need for new working capital, to be borrowed from the commercial banks, it was all so very unexpected. Right away the professional BL-knockers in the national newspapers (and there were any number of them by this time) set up ululations of 'we told you so', and repeated their allegations that the company had been guilty of under-investment for a number of years, and of having too many old models. The fact that several attractive-looking new models, like the wedge-styled Austin Princess, the Triumph TR7 sports car, the sleek and desirable Jaguar XJ-S coupé, and the Rover SD1 hatchback saloon were all in the wings, and working up towards release, was not generally known, but soon made a nonsense of this attitude.

The stark facts, however, were that the Corporation was in big trouble, that its profits had turned into losses, and that its reserves were draining away very rapidly and that it might soon be staring bankruptcy in the face. Everything, it seemed, was going wrong at once, and the news was mostly bad. Not only was the British market share down to 32 per cent (from 41 per cent in 1968), but Ford were about to launch their restyled Escort, and they also let it be known that their 'Bobcat' project (Fiesta, as it was eventually named) would join the battle for 'Supermini' sales in 1976).

Within weeks of Wedgwood-Benn's statement, however, it became clear that prospects were even more gloomy than ever. The Government-controlled National

. . . while this is already showing signs of the ADO88 style which matured in the next year or so.

Enterprise Board, whose chairman was Sir Don Ryder, was asked to make a fast, full and detailed study of British Leyland and its future prospects and to report back as soon as possible. The Ryder Report, as it became colloquially known, was ready before the end of April 1975 and proposed sweeping changes.

Financially, an immediate, though partial, nationalisation of the business was proposed whereby the NEB would allocate huge sums of money over the next four years. Existing shareholders, however, would only be offered 10p per share for holdings with a nominal value of 50p. (Soon after the formation of British Leyland, in 1968, these shares had soared to 80p and more . . ..) According to the forecasts, the Government's shareholding was likely to increase with every succeeding year.

The Government accepted the recommendations and a top-level management shake-up followed at once. Lord Stokes became non-executive President, while John Barber lost his job altogether. Alex Park, the company's finance chief, became chief executive, while Sir Don Ryder himself took over as chairman for a time. From October 1975 an independent chairman took over—Professor Sir Ronald Edwards (no relation to the next-but-one-chairman), who was president of Beechams, a director of ICI and Hill Samuel. Professor Edwards made the brave introductory remark—'British Leyland is a limited liability company which must be run as such, although it just so happens that the Government is a major shareholder', which cut little ice with anyone, especially the trade unions, because the government stake was already 90 per cent, and likely to increase every time a new tranche of finance was required.

There were thousands of brave words in the Ryder Report, most of which subsequently proved to have been written from false assumptions. Sir Don, the self-publicising workaholic, and his team, made many recommendations, most of which subsequently proved to have been taken from the existing Stokes-Barber strategic plan in any case! £1,264 million was proposed for capital expenditure, and £260 millions for working capital, to make British Leyland 'viable and fully competitive'. The Corporation would need funds from external sources from 1975 to 1981 of a further £1,400 million and Government would provide £800 millions of this by 1978.

The business was to be split up into four separate operations—Cars, Trucks and Buses, Special Products and International. The whole of the car-making activities were to be grouped together in Leyland Cars—Minis with Jaguars, Rovers with Marinas, MGs and Triumphs. It was their first major mistake. Nothing was more likely to destroy individual initiative than to see the separate divisions all dismantled. Marque identity was to be played down, as was the historical heritage of some locations.

(The Ryder Report actually made great play of the fact that 'the team considered and rejected the approach of dividing up the car operations into two or three separate divisions based on their products. They considered setting up Austin-Morris, Rover-Triumph and Jaguar, or a combination of ''volume cars'' (Austin-Morris) and ''Specialist cars'' (Jaguar-Rover-Triumph) . . . However, in the end they decided that a single integrated car business would best serve the Corporation in the future. Rationalisation of models, engines, transmissions and components are called for. They do not believe that a separate company structure for each car maker would allow this policy to be implemented'.)

In the next few years, of course, this policy was to be changed again and again. The vast 'Leyland Cars' organisation was speedily dismantled by Michael Edwardes at the beginning of 1978, with Austin-Morris being hived off from Jaguar-Rover-Triumph, and a short time afterwards Jaguar was given more operating freedom. In 1980, however, everything began to change again, with the establishment of the LMC (Light-Medium Cars) division to bring together all design, development, styling and planning activity of the Austin-Morris and Rover-Triumph businesses. How could a V8-engined Rover saloon be a 'Light-Medium' car? Don't ask anyone at BL—they get embarrassed about it. Have we heard the last of reorganisation? I doubt it.

While this upheaval was taking place, the dedicated management team at Longbridge were trying to get on with their jobs. Their major problem, however, was to know what that job was, for it was quite inevitable that there would be more delays while the new regime took control. Perhaps *Autocar*, commenting on the Ryder Report, and its aftermath, put it all into perspective: 'Ryder says the Mini must stay. An immense amount of work has already been done at Longbridge on replacement projects—but much of this work has gone to waste and it seems that at one time a decision was taken in principle not to replace the Mini at all. But the design is now 16 years old and events show signs of overtaking it just as they overtook the VW Beetle. Any replacement must be engineered from the start to offer the widest possible *real* choice without involving too much engineering change . . . but even the base ''Mini replacement'' should be rather larger than the present Mini'.

Their information, however, was not quite up to date. Work on one Mini replacement—ADO74—had indeed 'gone to waste', but work on a new project had already begun. ADO74 had been killed off, and the news had leaked out, but

ADO88 had been born. It was all a natural consequence of Harry Webster's departure from Longbridge.

In the last few months of British Leyland's existence as an independent concern, Spen King had been appointed Director of Product Development of BMC, which meant that he had to take ultimate technical responsibility for everything from a Mini replacement to a vast new Scammell tank transporter. As far as new car design was concerned he needed able deputies. Bob Knight retained control at Jaguar, John Lloyd took over at Rover-Triumph, and the new Director of Engineering at Longbridge was Charles Griffin.

Griffin was one of those long-serving heroes, a 'back-room' boy from pre-BMC days, who had been close to Alec Issigonis, and somewhat in his shadow, for many years. It was Griffin who had looked after BMC's more conventional cars while Issigonis was off on his flights of fancy with front-wheel-drive, transverse engines and Hydrolastic suspension, and it was Griffin who had served directly under Harry Webster in the first years of British Leyland control. He was a BMC, if not an 'Austin' man, through-and-through, and it was a popular appointment.

No one at Longbridge knew more about front-wheel-drive cars than Charles Griffin, and with nothing more than broad agreement from his directors, and from the fledgling Product Planning departments, he set about inspiring the birth of a new car. The requirements were clear—it was to be a direct replacement for the existing Mini, but it was to be that important bit larger, not physically as large as ADO74, but sensibly larger than the 10 foot car which had been around the scene for so long.

The Superminis, which strongly influenced the shaping of ADO74, were becoming more and more successful and significant, though no other concern built a full four-seater which was as small as the Mini and no one looked likely to try. Fiat's rear-engined 126 was about the same size, but didn't offer anything like as much passenger space.

The trends were obvious, for slightly larger cars like the Fiat 127, the Renault 5 and the Peugeot 104 were already on the market. More important, however, was the intelligence from overseas that the first-ever VW 'Supermini'—to be called the Polo—was also on its way.

All these cars had made their mark, and all were successful, but they were all considerably larger than the Mini, or even the long-nose Mini Clubman. The 'going rate' for the overall length of an average 1970s Supermini seemed to be about 11 feet 6 inches, built on a wheelbase of between 7 feet 8 inches and 8 feet (92 inches to 96 inches).

By BMC/British Leyland standards, this looked too large. Charles Griffin was convinced that there was no need for the next Mini to grow so much, not when its existing major dimensions were an overall length of 10 feet and a wheelbase of a mere 6 feet 8 inches (80 inches). The Austin Allego, which was much larger than the Mini, had only just gone on sale, with what British Leyland thought was the extremely generously proportioned wheelbase of 8 feet (96 inches). The engineers at Longbridge, along with the styling designers, could surely provide a new car with at least as much interior space (or, to use fashionable motor industry jargon, 'with the same package'), as the Superminis, but in a rather more compact outline.

Casual historians might get confused at some time in the future for spotting that Innocenti, with large factories in Italy, who were already building Minis under licence from British Leyland, surprised everyone by announcing a new car with smart Bertone styling on the basis of a Mini floorpan. There were two types of

Innocenti Mini on offer—the '90' with a 998 cc engine and rather basic trim and furnishing, and the '120' with a tuned-up single carburettor 1,275 cc engine (of 1275GT Mini type) and a more luxuriously appointed interior.

The most remarkable feature of the car—indeed, its entire *raison d'être*—was its styling, and layout. The Italian specialist coachbuilder, Bertone, had done a really remarkable job on the basis of the standard floorpan, suspensions and 12 inch 1275GT wheels and tyres. The overall length was 10 feet 3 inches—just three inches more than that of the original Mini, and slightly shorter than the Clubman—while the width was 4 feet 11 inches, 3.5 inches wider than the standard car.

Not only were the lines altogether smarter and more crisp than those of the original, but there was a hatchback third door (with a rather high sill) and folding rear seats. Other desirable extra touches included rear window wipe/wash, and through-flow ventilation. On the '120' version there were carpets on the floor, reclining front seats and a very smart full-width facia style featuring a full display of instruments and face-level eyeball-type air vents. Another forward-looking inprovement, not

Good try and commercially successful—in Italy. Bertone produced a completely new body style on a Mini floor pan, engine layout and suspensions. It was a crisp and attractive style for 1974—unfortunately it had less interior space than a Mini.

incorporated on any ordinary Mini, was the use of a front-mounted radiator with an electric cooling fan.

It was a very pretty little car which became an instant success in Italy, in spite of the fact that it had to sell directly against the mighty Fiat empire's 127. However, almost as soon as it was ready to go on sale, the new state-owned British Leyland combine began selling off overseas subsidiaries and Innocenti, which was one of these, was sold off to Alejandro de Tomaso, whose other Italian enterprises included de Tomaso cars and the Maserati group. From that time (1976) the car became a de Tomaso Mini, still with Innocenti badges, and was developed more and progressively more as the decade progressed.

Why was the Bertone style not adopted for use at Longbridge? It was certainly considered, and very carefully, but by the time the motoring press got wind of this the entire project had been abandoned. At a time when motoring magazines, and even some national newspaper correspondents, were not only suggesting that the Bertone style should be taken up by British Leyland, but that arrangements were

The Bertone Mini, later sold as a De Tomaso, with its hatch open. In Italy it was an interesting alternative to the domestic Fiat 127, but it was not roomy enough for BL to adapt for British manufacture in the late 1970s.

One way to get much more space into a Mini was to make its body wider—much wider! At the end of 1973, BL did just that, on the basis of the Clubman. Doesn't the wide car make the ordinary Clubman look narrow?

already being made to do so, they were more than a year out of date.

'We had a look at the idea of using the Bertone style or a development of it', Rex Fleming of Styling says, 'and there were various ways it could have been done. The style, as a style, appealed to us, but that was all.'

'The problem was the package', Harris Mann butted in. 'There was not more, but less, room inside than in a Mini, and that would never have done. Charles Griffin had laid down a minimum package for a new car, and the Bertone was a long way off.'

In particular, there was insufficient space in the rear and the body shell would have been considerably more expensive to build than the current Mini. In spite of the fact that panel sets were stamped in Britain, and shipped out to Italy for assembly, it seemed to make no sense to put the car into quantity production at Longbridge. Even 5,000 cars a year did not seem to be viable.

Before the end of 1974, in any case, the death of ADO74 had been forgotten, and the search for a new mini-car was under way. In the last days of the Stokes-Barber control of Longbridge, John Barber had revived his interest in the project, suggested that the new project should be a direct Mini replacement, and gave the go-ahead on that basis. When Sir Don Ryder and Alex Park took over in the spring of 1975 (and with Derek Whittaker becoming managing director of Leyland Cars), they agreed with this policy, and the 'new Mini' programme went ahead at full blast. At this stage, and all being well, the new model *could* have been ready by the end of 1978.

It all started with Charles Griffin, whose original brief to the designers, and to Tom Penny's styling department, was simple and extremely demanding. They should look for a direct Mini-replacement, using some carryover parts if necessary, which was to be little longer than the Clubman (10 feet 4.5 inches), and which was to have the best interior 'package' in the business. He didn't want it to be as big as the obvious Fiat/Renault/VW competition on the outside, but to match these cars, inch for inch, inside where the passengers could benefit.

It was a tall order. Not impossible, just very difficult. In layman's language, it had to be 'as small as a 'phone box outside, as large as the Albert Hall inside'. Harris Mann put it even better: 'The most important Commandment we had to obey was "Thou shalt not lose any package". So we coined the nickname Tardis—from *Dr Who*—a machine much bigger on the inside than the outside, and just got on with it'.

There was no doubt in Charles Griffin's mind—in anyone's mind—that the new car would have to be a three-door hatchback. It was the most fashionable layout, and it was the most practical one as well. He wanted to see more front-to-rear space from dash panel to rear seat squab (the original Mini's front seat had given a very upright driving stance), so he was willing to allow a longer wheelbase. But that allowance, from an engineer, was like drawing blood from Dracula. In nutsy-boltsy terms, inches cost money. At the time, in round terms, an extra inch in body length brought a 12 lb weight penalty. In width the problem was worse—an extra inch in width meant an extra 19 lb. Griffin and his planners had to grin and bear it—a larger Mini was going to be more Mini—heavier and more costly.

The vital wheelbase dimension? Open to final negotiation at this point, but around 87 to 89 inches. A code name? No problem—the ADO. . . series was still in use at this time and, since the ideal number had not yet been allocated, it might as well be 88. The new project, therefore, had a code—ADO88, which not only defined the latest replacement-Mini project, but specified the wheelbase as well.

By November 1974 the car was taking shape, it seemed, all over Longbridge. The two styling houses—the Elephant House and the older building—were busily sketching and carving away at models. In the design building, new in 1961 and already beginning to look, and feel, old-fashioned (such was the pace of motor industry technology), mechanical layouts were under way. In the Kremlin, and at British Leyland's headquarters in London's Marylebone Road, the financial planners were beginning to tot up large and potentially depressing sets of figures. In Longbridge, too, production engineers with many years of experience were taking yet another look at the sprawling layout of Longbridge, to see where the new car could be built. Somehow, the atmosphere was different. All the previous projects had looked ephemeral, but this one looked serious.

In technical terms, it was Big Decision time. For sure, the Mini's old rubber cone suspension was on the way out, but what would take its place? The designers were allowed to consider anything—anything, that is, which did not clash, or intrude, with Charles Griffin's package. Fred Coultas, appointed chief engineer of the product (a man with BMC/British Leyland design and development experience stretching back to 1961, and the very early days of 1100/1300 development) was even allowed to look again at the vexed question of engine, and transmission, layouts.

Longbridge's designers, indeed, had always been good at designing new engines, if not in getting them into production. The project alphabet started with A, B, and C— conceived in the 1950s and built by the million ever since. We never got to know

anything about 'D', but the next along was the overhead camshaft 'E' series, for the Maxi, and also for the Allegro. Then came the flood—some of which only existed on paper, some of which were actually built and tested—F, G, H, J, K, and so on. H-Series engines were typical BMC/British Leyland 'state-of-the-art' designs, with siamesed cylinder bores, a belt-driven single overhead camshaft, and a three bearing crank. It was engines like these which had been installed in Alec Issigonis' 9X project, and it was a 1.3-litre development, the K-Series, which was projected for

Opposite *ADO88, as a project, was already active by mid-1974. In July 1974, as the record card on the floor confirms, this full-size clay mock-up had two slightly different styles, split longitudinally down the centre of the car. 12 inch Mini-Clubman wheels were being used (top), but different 12 inch wheels were used on the near side of the mock-up (bottom). Elements of the definitive ADO88 shape are already beginning to emerge.* **Below** *Another ADO88 mock-up, also slightly different on left and right, photographed for the record on July 16 1974.*

OVERLEAF

Background photograph *By November 1974, just before British Leyland had to turn to the Government for financial assistance, the ADO88 project was being refined. This scene, in the 'old' styling studio at Longbridge, shows three full-size 'clays' lined up for inspection by management, with a standard Mini for comparison, and with an embryo ADO88 seating mock-up in the background. On this occasion, each mock-up is symmetrical from side to side.* **Inset left** *Style 'B' of November 13 1974, beginning to look more like the Metro now on sale, but not yet with such a well-defined nose.* **Inset right** *Style C, also of November 1974, had a vertical nose, and no obvious attempt at aerodynamic smoothing of the front of the car.*

25AD088 A 16 7 74 R

AD088 VEHICLE PACKAGE & SAFETY ENGINEERING

C

B

B

B ADO88 47 231174 R

C AD088 52 031174 R

Harry Webster's ADO74 project, which had bitten the dust a year before ADO88 was born.

None of the new engines, however, had been put into production, mainly because the investment required, and the tooling work which it would entail, was enormous. Further, any new engine would have to stay in production for 15 to 20 years, and would have to be used in several other models to make the project worthwhile. It was a big decision to make, and one which was not taken without a great deal of heart-searching.

Among the many options investigated was that of converting the old A-Series engine (as used in the Mini, the Allegro and the small-engined Marina models) to an overhead camshaft layout, and several prototypes were built and extensively tested in current models.

Fred Coultas comments: 'We'd done a lot of work on different engines, and got hold of competitors' engines, to see what they were capable of. We found that, apart from the fact that it was heavier, our A-Series was leading the field. This, by the way, was in the political climate of an energy crisis, where economy began to mean more than power'. The overhead-cam conversion certainly gave more power, but no better torque or operating economy.

Mark Snowdon, who became Director of Product Development at Austin-Morris somewhat later, put it very succinctly: 'You have to remember that although it's an old design, the 'A' is actually better than a lot of the new engines on specific fuel consumption and torque at moderate rpm . . . In some ways, high-revving ohc small engines with good specific power at high revs but less good at low, are less relevant than when they were introduced a few years ago. It's difficult to see how we could get, by what ever route, an engine with better specifics throughout the rev range, and better torque in the 1,500-2,500 rpm ranges . . .'.

'But we did recognise that we were in trouble with noise, and weight', Fred Coultas says, and so the bulk of work on engines for the new ADO88 was concentrated on making a better, quieter, more economical and more refined version of the existing A-Series unit. The tooling bill, in the end, was a massive £30 million, all of which was spent at Longbridge, in the East Works, and the result was the more robust, more powerful and more efficient A-Plus engine which has also found its way into the Ital, the last of the Allegros, and into the Mini (in modified form). There will also be a place for it in the next new BL car, coded LM10 at the time these words were being written, and to be assembled at the 'Morris' Cowley plant.

The same sort of reasoning—to balance investment against existing reputations and convenience, whether to design anew, or up up-date and modify what is already being built—was applied to the transmission. All previous transverse A-Series engine installations at British Leyland had featured the 'gearbox-in-sump' layout, so controversial when newly-announced in 1959, especially as the gearbox shared the same oil as the engine, but so very successful in the years which followed. As the world now knows, this layout, in improved form, was retained for the Metro. Why, then, have most other manufacturers, like Fiat and VW, not followed suit but designed new 'in-line' or 'end-on' gearboxes instead? Fred Coultas made it all clear: 'We stayed with the existing layout for very good packaging reasons. Fitting end-on gearboxes always gives you a width problem in the engine—we'd have had to find an extra six or seven inches across the engine bay—and that would mean using a different front suspension, probably a MacPherson strut layout'.

Designing a new car is like that. Change one thing, and at least two other features are affected. It's not only a three-dimensional space-juggling operation, but two extra dimensions also have to be considered—those of time and cost. See it done once, and one wonders how any new car ever reaches the showrooms at all. See it done several times, and one sees why some peoples' experiences are worth buying at a high price.

So, what sort of suspension was it to be? And what sort of springs were to be used? Hard, bouncy rubber cones like the Minis, Hydrolastic (rubber and liquid) suspension like the Maxis and 1100s, or Hydragas (the latest gas/rubber/liquid system) like the new Allegro and the Princess?

'We looked at everything—we had time to look at everything', Fred Coultas commented, 'from coil springs to torsion bars, and all the systems we already used at Longbridge. *As engineers* we all liked the VW Polo layout (MacPherson struts at the front, trailing arms and coil springs at the rear), which was simple, and cost effective. The problem was that it ruined the packaging at the rear!'

Packaging—that all-embracing word again. Charles Griffin's directive had been that the maximum possible space should be provided inside the car. He had to keep reminding people that cars were for carrying passengers and luggage and that the technical layout would have to be subservient to that.

The problem was that Griffin, and the styling engineers, wanted to have a really wide load space behind the seats, to match the big hatchback door they were planning. Conventional rear suspensions needed conventional dampers to control them. Dampers needed housings, housings needed covers, and trim—before you knew where you were, towers at each side of that load space were pushing in towards the middle of the car.

'To get the space we needed, it had to be a flat floor.' (Fred Coultas was rehearsing the thinking process). 'To get a flat floor we needed trailing arms and horizontal springs. To fit them in, and to satisfy the leverage ratio requirements, we had to use Hydrolastic or Hydragas. Hydragas was newer, and better, so we went for that. Which meant that we had to use Hydragas at the front as well. It was the best system anyway, so we had an ideal solution.'

Now, with the major decisions taken, it was time to start building the cars. Not real ones—not for months to come—but cars which could shake down the new designs, locate teething troubles and get on with testing. At British Leyland, the first cars are called Simulators, often existing models modified underneath, so that nobody even knows they are non-standard.

Keeping the new designs secret is important, especially these days, when industrial spies seem to be everywhere. When the Morris Marina had been developed at the end of the 1960s, the Cowley development team bought a fleet of Vauxhall Vivas, grafted Marina floor pans and suspensions underneath, and got on with the job in double quick time. For the ADO88 project, the problem was solved even easier. A word went out to the sales staff and the production engineers at Longbridge. A few days later, a small fleet of shiny new Allegros arrived in the workshops. Days later the conversion work was under way, and in May 1975 the first ADO88 Simulator took to the road.

Note the date—May 1975. Even though the Ryder Report had only just been published, and even though the new top names and faces were only just making their mark, the 'Replacement Mini' was on its way. But it was already clear that it couldn't possibly go on sale in 1978, even though the first Birmingham NEC Motor Show of October 1978 would have been a perfect publicity springboard. The change of management made it inevitable, for every project had to be examined, vetted and

A year later, in November 1975, ADO88 was assuming more importance in the 'Ryder' company's produce plan. **Above** *This was one proposed version, with a rather upright nose.* **Below** *This was another, which was getting quite close to the style of ADO88 eventually adopted.*

submitted to the National Enterprise Board. Even though it meant that the new car would not appear for more than four years, the projected launch date was put back to 1979.

In the meantime, the technicians and artists in the Longbridge styling studios were as busy as ever. Not only were they beavering away at the development of ADO88, but they had other projects to keep them busy. Even though the wedge-nosed Princess was now well behind them, there was still MGB 'facelift' work to be considered, work on the long-wheelbase Triumph Lynx (based on the TR7 sports car) and even thoughts of a completely new body shape for the Morris Marina.

Harris Mann, British Leyland's top 'exteriors' stylist, was working ridiculous hours by now. At one moment he would be in his studio, sketching ideas for the latest car, and at another he would be out on the modelling floor, seeing how the models were taking shape. But that wasn't all. There were meetings—many meetings, lengthy meetings—with manufacturing specialists, cost analysts, product planners and sales managers. Producing a new car is not quick, nor is it easy. Mann, not for the first time in his professional life, was finding this yet again.

'We start with sketches, lots of them', Harris Mann said, 'from which we select one, two or perhaps three themes to develop. Sketches are easy—we can do several in a day—but getting them built up into three-dimensional clay takes more time. In this case, with ADO88, the package requirements gave us the biggest headache of all. We could so easily have finished up with an orange box on wheels, a very plain car, something like the Fiat Panda.'

Charles Griffin's package requirement, indeed, were causing all sorts of problems—not because they were impractical, but because they automatically meant that the new car had to be larger than the existing Mini. Firstly, he insisted that the new car should have equal front and rear tracks—the Mini had a narrower rear track which limited rear seat and stowage space. Next he specified a longer 'passenger box' *and* a wider one into the bargain. To use a modern phrase, he wanted the new car to be 'space efficient'. Just to illustrate the point, and to see if it was even a practical idea, he had a much wider Mini Clubman built. He proved his point, but the result— eight inches wider, but the same in all other major respects—looked very strange.

By the autumn of 1975, ideas had begun to gell, but not until after a great deal of thought, negotiation and new ideas. David Bache, Rover's renowned styling director, took over control of all Leyland Cars styling during the year and brought yet another expert view to the project. Harris Mann had been working towards a new car which was quite utilitarian in its aspect ('We were producing something of a two-box estate car style, which was *very* functional, still something of a 'Plain Jane', but we *were* satisfying that very demanding package . . .') and Bache wanted to get more form, and more interest, into the body panels.

More full size clays—different on one side from the other—were sculpted, but still Bache, and the Longbridge department chief, Tom Penny, were not satisfied. Bache was still somewhat worried about its lack of identity and decided to call in a consultant. Michelotti had been invited to produce cars in the ADO74 period, but now it was the turn of Pininfarina, from Turin.

Pininfarina's suggested style, as a full-size clay, arrived in Britain on 18 December 1975, and was hustled up to Solihull, where rival offerings were put on display. Sergio Pininfarina himself was met in London by Spen King and Alan Edis (Product Planning Director at this time) and driven up to the Rover factory, where a midnight viewing took place, along with the directors of Leyland Cars.

Above *Pininfarina, the famous Italian styling house, was asked to prepare a 'Supermini' style towards the end of 1975, and this was the result. It featured 10 inch Mini wheels, rather obvious styling ridges around the rear quarters and a very complex nose/headlamp/bumper layout. It was rejected because it would have been too expensive to build.* **Below** *The ADO88 mock-up already depicted (page 54, below), lined up in the 'Elephant House' at Longbridge, alongside a Bertone-styled Mini, which was already in production in Italy. The difference in package size is very obvious.*

Once viewed alongside the latest offerings from Longbridge, the Pininfarina offering was soon rejected, because its nose was thought to be too 'fussy', and because it would have been too costly to build. No more outside help was ever again requested for this programme—from this point, Harris Mann's designers were allowed to develop their own ideas.

Of all the full-size clay models prepared during the year, a styling theme selection had been made in October 1975. This, according to the convention used in all British styling houses, had only been one side of a particular model, so in the next four months a new model—the same at both sides on this occasion—was carefully shaped, and final exterior approval followed in February 1976. At last—or was it?— almost everyone seemed to be happy.

The development workshops, in any case, had not been able to wait. Once the car's wheelbase had been settled—87 inches in the beginning, but moving up to 88.6 inches as detail development continued—the craftsmen were ready to start building cars, and, by the summer of 1975, delays were no longer possible. The first ADO88 prototypes—SEPs (Semi-Engineered Prototypes) in Longbridge industrialese—took shape in the next few weeks, and in November 1975 the first took to the roads.

Why the wheelbase change? It was all accommodated ahead of the doors for, as Fred Coultas recalls: 'We eventually changed our carburettor installation, which needed just that important bit of extra space behind the engine, we needed more space for the exhaust downpipes, and we also wanted a bit more crushability in the body shell to meet legal requirements. A bonus was that, by pushing the front wheels forward by 1.6 inches, we gained a little bit more leg room around the pedals, at the toeboard.'

For the development engineers, the problem now was not so much one of making

Above *Almost the same pose as the previous picture, but with different cars. This shows two cars; a conventional Mini against the ADO88 style which had just received 'theme approval' for further refinement in November 1975.*

Below left *How to confuse the opposition! This prototype ADO88 not only had cardboard panels masking the shape of the windows, but also had a different, ugly, glass-fibre bonnet panel and an extra mock-up front grille.* **Below** *It also had a boot 'bustle' and generally was about as ungainly as it was possible to arrange.*

Above *Even towards the end of ADO88/Metro testing, the old cars were still being used for development purposes. This car was an FEP, in use at BL's new Gaydon proving grounds, on Brake Test work, still with a high, flat, bonnet line.*

the cars work, and work well, but keeping them secret. It wasn't that the replacement-Mini project was completely unknown—far from it, for now that British Leyland was a state-owned concern, every MP, lobbyist, economic pundit, or media busybody seemed to consider himself an expert on the subject, and sounded off at regular intervals—but that it was hoped that the competition, especially Ford, would be kept in the dark as long as possible. Even though the SEPs weren't being built to the finalised shape, they were close enough to the theme to make recognition unwise.

The usual way to disguise a prototype is to make it look like a delivery van—(do you remember a famous Father Brown story, where the murderer was a postman, and no one ever looks at a postman? The same applies to vans in the motor industry!)—or a pick-up with a canvas roof or 'tilt'. The alternative is to play childish games, and smother the metal panels with false glass fibre, or even cardboard shapes. If you saw something like this on the roads around Longbridge, or on the M5 motorway towards Bristol, it was probably an ADO88 on test. Until 1979, when BL's new proving ground at Gaydon, south of Warwick, finally opened, they had to take their chances and go out on public roads far too often for their liking.

Once a project as big as this gets past the styling approval stage, it picks up a

Above *ADO74 project of 1973/1974—the true ancestor of the ADO88 Supermini, which never progressed beyond the mock-up stage.* Below *January 1974, and one possible treatment for the 'new Mini' evolves.* Bottom *Project leader Harris Mann found time to sketch this theme for the rapidly-developing ADO88 'Supermini' in August 1975.*

Above *The full-size ADO88 mock-up, as approved, at the beginning of 1976. Note the simple door-opening arrangements, and the rather upright tailgate. There was no aerodynamic front spoiler at this point.* **Below** *Autumn 1977, and changes to the ADO88 begin to stack up before a full-blooded restyle, into LC8, begins. This was the 'interim' solution proposed and included a front spoiler, re-shaped rear wheel arch cut outs, and conventional door handles.* **Bottom** *The definitive LC8, with more shape in the sides, a more sloping tailgate and more familiar Metro details. This shape can be compared directly with that at the top of this page.*

Above *A rather way-out theme proposal for a Supermini facia, but its links with the real thing are obvious.* **Below** *This looks real doesn't it? In fact, it is a wood, clay and plastic mock-up of the proposed Metro facia, ready for final approval on July 12 1978.*

Above *The LC8, still un-named, at the Paris 'clinic' in January 1978, where the public was able to compare it with cars like the Renault 5, the Ford Fiesta and the Fiat 127. This was the breakthrough for BL, after all the 'clinic' disappointments of 1977.*

Above left *Pre-programmed, automatic welding in progress in the New West Works at Longbridge on a Metro body shell.*

Left *Making the Metro body shell—one of the lines of robots which carry out hundreds of spot welding operations on every car going through the New West Works at Longbridge.*

Above *ADO88, as approved for refinement in November 1975 by the 'Ryder' management, including Alex Park (chairman) and Derek Whittaker (managing director, Leyland Cars).* **Below** *To refine the chosen ADO88 theme, the stylists thought they could make improvements, and this was a sketch of what was intended.*

The finalised ADO88 style, from which engineering body drawings would be made, was completed early in 1976. Compared with the ADO88 selected at 'theme approval' (page 65, above), it had a slightly longer wheelbase (there is a larger gap between wheel arch cut outs and the door pillar), revised bumpers, inset headlamps, different road wheels (still 12 inch) and also had details like door locks and air-intake grilles added.

momentum of its own, and department after department is inexorably sucked in. To an outsider, it looks chaotic, but to a seasoned motor industry observer it is a fascinating and logical process. Even before the stylists had done their job, they had called in Body Engineering, Chassis Engineering, Trim, Hardware, and Electrical Engineering, the materials specialists, the factory equipment planners, the quality control engineers, the Product Cost Control staff and the sales force. Product Planning, naturally, were always involved. The days of design, development and inspiration by one man are long gone. Nowadays every car, in every firm, is a committee job. The miracle is that some new cars still have a discernible character and, in the case of the ADO88 project, there was a lot of that.

By the middle of 1976, all ten Semi-Engineered Prototype ADO88s had been completed, and the project was steaming ahead. Money had been committed— hundreds of millions of pounds—tooling was about to begin and thoughts had already turned to the manufacturing site for the car. Everyone, it seemed, now knew that a new mini-sized car was on the way, but no one yet seemed to be saying much about it. Even in his early interviews, Derek Whittaker was only willing to beat the drum, proclaim his faith in Leyland Cars' future, and promise that the car would be right, in 1979. The launch date was firmly fixed for October 1979—a year, incidentally, in which there would be no motor show in Britain.

By the summer of 1977, the first of the Fully-Engineered Prototype ADO88s (FEPs, in Longbridge-language), was ready for the road, and there would be 17 of these cars altogether. In every shape, every corner, in every panel joint, they looked like the shape finally approved in the styling department. The difference between

SEPs and FEPs was dramatic ('They're usually as different as chalk and cheese'—Fred Coultas), for SEPs have hand-crafted body panels and FEPs have panels pressed from temporary 'soft' tools.

It was a time for purposeful activity, and a time for reflection. One week there would be a programmed barrier crash test (would the body be strong enough?), and the next week there might be a management viewing (what changes would be demanded, even at this late stage?). Some engineers would be undertaking fuel economy tests, or sorting out brake materials, not a very exciting process. Others might be flogging up and down hot Italian autostradas, in 90 degree temperatures, to prove the cooling and the ventilation.

According to all the rules, the design should be settling down and the work should be becoming routine. But not this time—not for the ADO88. The first doubts were beginning to creep in, and the criticisms came from several directions. Within weeks the atmosphere at Longbridge had changed yet again. The mood had changed. ADO88 was not right. Was it too late to have it changed?

A much-modified ADO88 Fully-Engineered Prototype (FEP), as used for testing. This car has had the latest (LC8/Metro) front spoiler added and is ready for viewing in the styling studios.

Chapter 4

The birth of the Metro
The big rethink and LC8

The glass-fibre mock-up of ADO88 was pushed into the secret styling 'clinic' at The Hague, in Holland, on August 25 1977. It was white, had no badges, and was impossible to identify. Also in the display were its competitors—a Fiat 127, a Ford Fiesta, a Honda Civic, and a Mini Special—also white, also unbadged.

It was the sort of consumer test which most car companies now carry out when they have a new model under development. Those invited to take part had been carefully chosen by market research specialists—either as small-car owners, or as typical customers for this type of car. More than 200 of them would see these cars in the next few days, and would be asked several questions. The most important ones were: Do you like the exterior style? Do you like the overall concept—the package? Would you buy one? None of them, it was hoped, would guess that they were looking at a new British Leyland design.

The results were discouraging. A few days later, the company repeated the 'clinic' in Dusseldorf, where a VW Polo and a Renault 5 were present, and in Paris, where the Renault 5 and the Fiesta were the most important rivals. In every country there was the same reaction. The ADO88 was not liked and something would have to be done.

After two years of development, this was a bitter blow. Perhaps it was all summed up by what happened to the mock-up as it was being manhandled out of the hall in Holland. On the way from the viewing area to the covered wagon, one of the wheel supports broke, and before it settled in the van, the wheel was off altogether. No detailed analysis was needed to sift the response to the car, for most returned questionnaires made the same points—the package was fine and the detail fittings were well-liked, but the style was not. By comparison with its rivals, most critics thought ADO88 was too plain, too flat-sided, too utilitarian.

Four years later, Harris Mann clearly remembers what impressions were gained from the clinic: 'There had been two major reactions. One was that the car was seen as having an excellent package and function—we were certainly moving in the right direction. That was the good news. The second was that the style was seen as too austere, somewhat slab-sided, and even a bit ugly around the back end. The big hatchback was liked for access, but people thought it was too upright.'

It is easy to be wise after the event, but now there seems to be no doubt that several people, and departments, had all begun to have their doubts by the summer of 1977. In financial terms, it was Big Decision time again, for the excavators had already broken ground on extensions to Longbridge and some of the body panel press tooling had already been ordered.

There was nothing amiss with ADO88 as it stood (indeed, new competitive designs from Honda (the City) and VW (the revised Polo) both look remarkably like ADO88 in one way or another), it was just that the market place, and circumstances, seemed to have drifted away in the last two years. Customers, it seemed, were beginning to look for more style, more equipment, and more comfort in their smaller cars. In product planning terms, the demand for mini cars was going down, while that for the small cars was getting larger all the time. In Product Planning terms, you understand, a small car isn't a small car at all, but one which is bigger than a mini car . . ..

British Leyland's management had many other problems to face, mostly industrial and financial, but they also had to face up to the dilemma of the ADO88. Money had already been committed for tooling, and to cancel everything would be disastrous for morale. In the two years since ADO88 had started to take shape, almost everything seemed to have gone wrong. Public ownership had done nothing for the mood of the militant workforce, particularly at Longbridge, and Leyland Cars' share of the UK market had dropped from 31 per cent to 24 per cent. The company's first chairman as a nationalised company, Professor Sir Ronald Edwards, had died suddenly in January 1976, and his successor, Sir Richard Dobson, had fallen foul of the do-gooders with an indiscreet speech made at a so-called private dinner in October 1977. Quite unfairly, Sir Richard was branded as a racist and felt bound to resign. At the very moment when Leyland Cars needed every possible support, it found itself without a chairman.

It was about this time that a major reappraisal of policy began to take place and I should make it clear that Derek Whittaker, who was to leave the company in a matter of months, was one of its most influential supporters. As the heads were counted, as the numbers were added up, and as more and more clinic opinions became available, a major shift in emphasis for the project became inevitable. ADO88 was in trouble. Would it survive the next few weeks, and, if so, in what form?

Perhaps, it was argued, Charles Griffin's rigid package had been a shade too restrictive? Perhaps the new car should not be a straight replacement for the Mini after all? Perhaps it should be different, a bit larger, and better equipped than hitherto? Perhaps it should not be built down to a price, but up to a fine new standard?

But how much should be changed? How much *could* be changed? Could the original launch date still be met? *Should* it still be met? 'For the next few weeks, I don't think I've ever worked so hard—or so often', Harris Mann says. 'It was almost like tackling a face-lift on a car which had already been announced. But this job had to be finished in six weeks, no more, and even then we were sure that it was going to delay the launch.'

Rex Fleming, his boss, with many years of experience in the styling business, had never experienced anything as dramatic, certainly not at such a late stage, at so critical a point: 'We talked to a lot of people at great length, and while we were being asked what we thought should be done, we in turn were asking what *could* be changed if necessary. Some very large and major panels had already been designed, and released for press tool construction to begin—notably the entire floor pan and the door inner panels. The roof panel and the bonnet pressing were also well on the way.'

This is always the problem with the design of a new car—that it takes longer to prepare some parts for volume production than others. Because of the size, the complication and the delicate profiling required, the biggest steel pressings, and the facia mouldings, have to be finalised first of all. There are 'timing' specialists in every firm whose job it is to make sure that everything will, eventually, be ready at the right time and nowadays—need I say it—computers are used to help the planning. Massive pressings, like the floor pan and the inner door panels which Rex Fleming mentioned, are 'released' (that's motor industry slang for 'approved for production, and for tooling to start') up to 30 months—*two-and-a-half years*—ahead of the start of full production. From this point the 'releasing' process is continuous, and the last items of all to be approved are badges and ornamentation ('No one can every make their minds up about badges . . .'), between six months and nine months from 'Job One'.

Since, at this time, the ADO88 was meant to start production in the summer of 1979, ready for an autumn launch, it meant that work had started on the floor pan and the door inners at the beginning of 1977. The shaping of presses, and the design of jigs to fit panels together, had already been under way for the best part of a year, and dozens of other components were also being prepared as well.

It was one of those nightmares which big businessmen often have to face. Should they stop the job, cancel the tooling and start again, thereby wasting well over a year, a lot of money and a mountain of design talent? Or should they press on with the car which was being prepared, even though public opinion about its merits was divided? Would they have to delay the launch, or could they somehow keep to the original timetable? Was there, indeed, a half-way house which would make the best of the dilemma?

The Marketing Research department, which had been at the very centre of this storm since the first series of clinics were held, put everything in perspective, in a document written on October 24 1977, which summed up the alternatives as follows:

Route '0', to be tackled in a mere 10 days, was to investigate exterior changes without altering *any* body panels—in other words, a pure 'dress-up' job.

Route '1', with a four week target for completion, was to examine alterations to body side panels, the screen and the waistline, but not to include any modification to the rear or to the hatchback. For this change, a revised launch date of March 1980 was proposed.

Route '2', for which five week's work was to be allowed, was to add to the Route '1' changes by considering additional modifications to the rear end and hatchback, to make the car look altogether larger and sleeker than before. A revised launch date was not spelt out, but it was generally agreed that this would result in even more delay, perhaps until the autumn of 1980.

Because of the incredibly short time allowed, this was a very tall order, but the Styling division put aside every other job on which they were working, and concentrated on the ADO88's problem. At the start, a fourth modification was also considered, which was really Route '0' with reshaped wheelarch cut-outs, which had come in for particular criticism on the ADO88 at clinic viewing. Way back in 1974, in the original brief for a direct Mini replacement, the stylists and engineers had been told to consider the use of 10 inch and 12 inch road wheels—the smallest wheels, of Mini type, to be confined to the cheaper, down-market, versions of the new car, and the 12 inch wheels to be used on derivatives with higher performance where bigger wheels were desirable. This always creates a problem for planners, who must leave space in the wheel arch for the largest wheels (with snow chains fitted—a requirement in certain European countries), for the 10 inch wheels then looked somewhat 'lost' in a cavernous space.

It must have been at about this time when the new car began to take on its own individual character, not as a direct Mini replacement—not as a 'mini car' in product planning terms, but as a new and complementary BL cars model, a 'small car' to sell alongside the Mini, which would remain in production. It made a great difference to what followed in the next few weeks.

Management very quickly decided that Route '1' was not appropriate, and reduced their options to two—the quick 'dress-up' which might *just* allow the original October 1979 launch to be maintained, or the complete reskinning of the body shell, accompanied by a slight, but definite, move up-market in size, specification or price.

Even though there was precious little time to produce new styles (to save time, clay was actually built up on one of the existing ADO88 fibre-glass mock-ups before a completely new clay model was started), fleeting thought was once again given to the idea of producing an ultra-plain, ultra-functional style, where sheer packaging volume and utility could take precedence over that of status and decoration, but this was soon dismissed.

In the end, by furious application, much overtime ('I recall more than one all-night session—that's not usual, even in our business', Harris Mann told me), and by ruthless cutting of the normal timescale, two full-size clay models, with different styles on each side, were viewed, modified, discussed and approved. From them, two new full-size models, one coded '0A' with limited ADO88 modifications, and one '2B', which was almost a complete redesign, were produced.

It's fair to say that by this time several influential people in Leyland Cars were getting agitated. Suppose the public *still* didn't like what they saw? Suppose, somehow, that the whole concept of this car was not acceptable? Were Longbridge's stylists and engineers completely wrong, completely out of touch?

It was time to let the public have another look—time for another clinic. Once again four competitive vehicles were produced, and this time *both* the latest British Leyland styles were placed among them. Not one, but two different groups of consumers were asked to look at the cars—one group because they owned cars of the down-market ADO88 variety, the other group because their cars, and their social aspirations, were that important bit more up-market. The location, this time, was Bournemouth, and 400 people were involved. Which style would attract most people?

Mark Snowdon, recently appointed Director of Product Development, never had any doubts. Neither, for that matter, did the clinic visitors. With no less emphasis than before, they turned down the original ADO88 style, but with almost equal agreement, they flocked round the new car, and approved of it.

Leyland Cars directors had seen the re-shaping of the car during those frenetic weeks in October, November and December 1977, but the proposal for the new style was finally put to them on December 20 1977. This time there were no doubts, and no second thoughts. They liked the style and they chose it for final refinement; they also realised, understood and agreed that there would have to be a delay in the production tooling timetable and put off the launch until October 1980. At a stroke, almost, a year had been lost—which meant that the new car would not be available until the nationalised concern had been in existence for more than five years—but now the launch could not have been scheduled for a better time. It was now to coincide with the opening of the prestigious, but bi-annual, British motor show, at the National Exhibition Centre, on the outskirts of Birmingham.

For the sake of posterity, I ought to make it clear that this major decision, perhaps the most important in the history of Longbridge since Sir Leonard Lord had agreed to go ahead with the *original* Mini, was made effectively by 'pre-Michael Edwardes' management. In December 1977, Leyland Cars, as set up by Sir Don Ryder in 1975, was still in existence, and Derek Whittaker was its managing director. No sooner had the revised car got moving, however, when Michael Edwardes' policy of de-centralisation took shape, and it became an Austin-Morris, rather than a Leyland Cars, project.

In the meantime, Ray Horrocks, ex-Ford Motor Co high-flyer, and having recently had several years in the Eatons axles and transmissions group, became Whittaker's deputy, and it was no surprise when Whittaker himself resigned early in January 1978. Mark Snowdon, therefore, presented his formal proposal to Ray Horrocks, not to Derek Whittaker, at the beginning of the year. 'I told him that we should not replace the Mini, but that we should build a somewhat larger car which would be the leader in the 1980s. Ray Horrocks therefore stopped the ADO88 dead just at the critical point, and approved the new car'.

Those words are culled from a *Daily Express* interview at the time of the Metro's launch, over-simplifying what was, in fact, a more formalised process. By this time, indeed, ADO88 had already died, in favour of a new project, coded LC8. The 'Austin Drawing Office' codes had, at last, been superseded and 'Leyland Cars' codes took over. But why LC8? No one now knows, but the suggestion is that the number '8' was chosen merely for continuity purposes—certainly there never has been a project in the LC1 to LC7 range, though what is now the Triumph Acclaim was briefly called LC9, and the new range of middle-sized cars which follows Metro has always been known as LC10.

On January 16 1978, just as Leyland Cars was about to disappear in favour of the smaller car groupings, the LC8 full-size mock-up (this time a see-through version) was put on display in a Paris hotel, alongside a Ford Fiesta, a Renault 5, a Fiat 127 and a VW Polo. The invited public loved it, as did another group of consumers who saw the car in Rotterdam, later in the month. There were no hang-ups, and no different attitudes from country to country—LC8 was a viable 'European' car, which seemed to stand up very well against its competition. So now, the die was cast—ADO88 was dead. Long live LC8!

Thus it was that the new car, soon dubbed the Mighty Mini by management and press alike, took shape in the winter of 1977 to 1978. In no more than 14 weeks, a period which included the disruptive effects of Christmas and the New Year holidays, the small car project had been reviewed. In September 1977, it had looked desperate, but in January 1978 it all looked very promising.

Steven Schlemmer, who took charge of the Product Planning of LC8 at about this time, agreed that the opinions expressed at the clinics in 1977 were a very important factor in the speedy redesign, but also insisted that the changes were also made because the car's future role became better and better defined. In particular, it became more and more clear that the Mini should not be replaced, but that the new LC8 should be introduced to run alongside it: 'The LC8 was perhaps ''half-a-class''

Above *Part way through the crash restyling programme of October/November 1977, the sleeker, more rounded, LC8 clay model takes shape.* **Below** *The same model, very early in 1978, coming to the end of the massive and agonising reappraisal which followed ADO88's poor showings at 'clinic' in the summer of 1977.*

bigger in exterior dimensions, but in terms of function, space and refinement it's a whole class bigger, even with pretensions towards the class above that . . . .'

Would the Mini continue or not? This was a question often discussed at Longbridge and at corporate headquarters. No long-term plan drawn up at this time ever envisaged the Mini continuing for more than two or three years, but it was a car which always survived, and seemed to have a life, and a will, of its own. It was a car which created a great deal of emotion among customers, and the management, and seemed to be impervious to outside pressures. Like VW with the long-running Beetle, BL were to find out that it was going to be very difficult to replace.

By 1978, for sure, it had been decided that Mini was going to continue, and new facilities at Longbridge were being built alongside, rather than instead of, those already building parts for the car. The OPEC crude oil price rises of 1979, which were equally as devastating as those which caused the original Energy Crisis of 1973, did wonders for the Mini's image, for small fuel-efficient cars became more fashionable than ever before. The new management of BL Cars began to look on Mini as the tiny town car, the manoeuvrable and economical run-about, or even the second car, while LC8 took on more and more promise as a true family car, whose small size would be no restriction to its use on regular long journeys.

It was the style changes which made so much difference to the new car's prospects. Perhaps it should be emphasised that in the quick metamorphosis of ADO88 into LC8, there was no change to the basic engineering layout, suspension systems, engine and transmission, and seating provisions, nor were there more than very minor changes to the interior package—the space for passengers, pets and luggage.

Below *This is a typical full-size engineers' layout drawing, showing the finalised LC8. Note the position of the fuel tank,* under *the rear seat, and the small space taken up by the transverse engine.* **Opposite** *Front and rear view full-size drawings of the LC8/Metro, as finalised.*

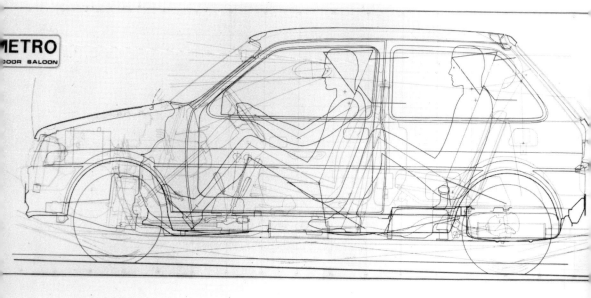

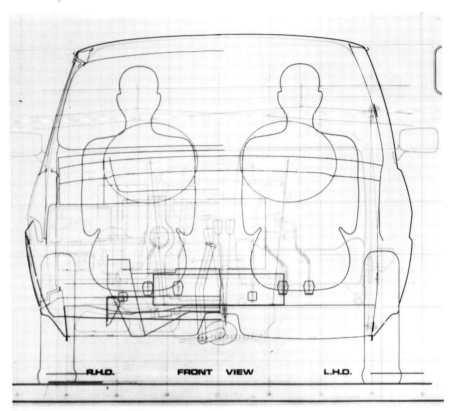

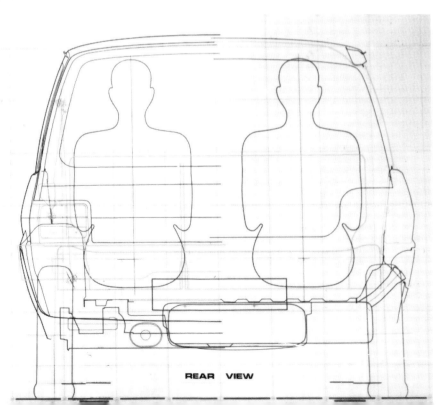

Almost all the changes were to the exterior style, to the 'presence' or the 'persona' of the machine itself.

In broad terms, LC8 was 2.5 inches longer than ADO88 had been, about two inches wider, and almost exactly the same height. Because of the decision to improve the specification, and to change the marketing intentions to a rather more complete, and costly, level, there was no provision for 10 inch wheels. All in all, the major difference was not in what the car could do, but in what it looked like.

The long-running philosophical argument over style had finally been won by those wanting a more shapely machine, and one which would more easily stand out from the 'Supermini' crowd. Although there was no doubt that it would have been cheaper to build an ultra-simple, ultra-functional car, it seemed that the public did not want such a car. Looking back, with hindsight, it is interesting to see that Fiat (and Giugiaro) chose the opposite approach with their new Panda Supermini—and interesting to see that in Britain, at least, this car has not sold well.

Though the general shape of the ADO88 was retained, every skin panel was changed in evolving LC8 and, in particular, the shape around the rear of the car was modified. Although the very useful feature of a full-depth tailgate, with the opening all the way down to the rear bumper level, and with the tail lamps stacked up in the corner, was retained, the rather upright profile was not. A second careful look at ADO88, as finalised, persuaded the stylists that there was, if anything, too much loading volume behind the rear seats. Accordingly, for LC8, the lower part of the tail, up to the level of the waistline, was a touch further back behind the rear wheels, while the rear corner, where the roof turned down into tailgate, was pulled slightly forward. Whereas ADO88 had featured a single curving profile at the rear, LC8 had a more pronounced forward-leaning shape above the waistline. It was that change, more than any other, which transformed the looks.

The aerodynamically efficient wedge nose, sweeping down from a normal windscreen position to a smoothly styled wide grille, was not changed in concept, but refined in detail, and the aerodynamic spoiler under the front bumper, which had not featured in the ADO88s viewed at clinics in 1977, was finally added to the specification. By leaning the plane of the hatchback forward, the side-view profile had also been made sleeker and there was a different balance to the glass area. Major skin panel changes along the side—like the more obvious barreling of the panels, and the more sculptured look given to them, the more pronounced wheel arch flares and the different rear wheel arch profile—were all obvious, but there were other detail changes to add to the attraction. For the LC8, for instance, conventional lift-up door handles were specified, in place of the controversial button arrangement of the ADO88, where the door pull was actually the edge of the door itself (with the side panel behind it being recessed to allow space for a curving hand). Somehow, the LC8 had been made into a 'softer', less utilitarian, car than ADO88 had been and this seemed to make it more appealing to those who viewed it.

At the same time, a blitz had also been carried out on the interior mock-ups of the car. The seats had been re-shaped, and made to look more substantial, the facia style was made to look even more comprehensive and clear to read than before and extra luxury items were made available. By this time there was no doubt in any planner's mind—LC8 would have to be better, quieter, smoother, and visually more attractive than any of its opposition.

A lot of work had gone into making the interior as practical, and versatile, as possible when the original ADO88 project was being developed and none of this was

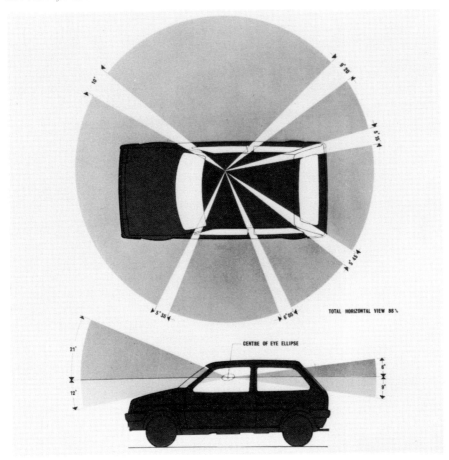

Visibility from the driving seat of the Metro is excellent. The only small blind spots are those six narrow white slices evident in the plan view.

to be lost with LC8. As with any hatchback, the rear seats would have to fold down into an 'estate car' position. There was nothing new in this—every other hatchback in the world provided the same feature. BL's designers, however, had thought it through. Not only had they considered a rear parcel shelf that would fold away into a small space, but they had considered stowing it to the back of the seat when not needed; in cars which competed with the LC8, such as the Ford Fiesta or the VW Polo, this was not provided.

The real breakthrough, however, was in the way the rear seat accommodation could be varied. Other hatchback cars, even their most costly derivatives, featured backrests which folded down in one piece—good and useful, for sure, but not very versatile. Perhaps the designers at Longbridge looked carefully at Ford's new Capri II sports saloon of 1974, or perhaps they thought it up for themselves. No matter—the ADO88 and LC8 models always had the provision for split folding of the backrests.

But, at Longbridge, even that was too conventional—too obvious. The real stroke of genius, which cost nothing, and gained a lot, was to make seat-folding asymetric—the split was not in the centre of the car, but well over towards the left side (near-side for a British-market car). This meant that it was possible to fold down the small 'half' of the backrest to increase stowage space, but still install two children or slim (and willing!) adults alongside—or to fold down the larger slab, at the other side, still have room for one person to ride in the back seat, and to have a sizeable platform for bulky packages, or a carrycot, even the bag of golf clubs, alongside. Brilliant, practical and universally praised.

Once the big decision had been taken—to cancel ADO88 after three years of active development, and to take up the new LC8 car, which was different in so many ways—there was a cost to be counted. It is to the credit of everyone concerned—workforce, management, directors and government backers—that morale did not seem to flag for an instant. We now know that 495,000 man-hours (costing £1.9 millions in labour costs alone) had been expended on ADO88 in 1975 and 1976, and that in 1977 the combined projects accounted for 267,000 man-hours and £1.5 millions. In the event, the car on which the money had been spent did not go into production in the same form, but no one, I am sure, would now call the effort a waste.

The main problem, indeed, was not now one of money, but one of time. Even before the ADO88 project had run into trouble, its readiness for launch in the autumn of 1979 had been in doubt. It might perhaps have been possible to show the car at that time, but there was still no guarantee that cars would have been ready for sale by then. Now, after a four-month hiatus in the major development process, a postponement was inevitable. No power available to BL—money, man-power *or* technological assistance—could hold it off.

Harold Musgrove, who had been drafted in from Bathgate as Manufacturing Director of Austin-Morris at the beginning of 1978, remembers the quandary clearly: 'Ray Horrocks and I walked around the Longbridge site in February or March 1978, when New West Works was still just steelwork and a bit of cladding. Ray, who never beats about the bush, said: ''Forget the launch date you've been told. Go away and time the job, time what still has to be done. When can we have the car ready?''

'I went right through the plans with my people, for about another month, then told Ray we could launch in October 1980, which coincided with the NEC Motor Show. There was no point in trying to cut corners, and telling him we could launch in August 1980, which was still two months away from the NEC Show, and there was *certainly* no point in saying we could be ready in November 1980. That would have been too late! It couldn't be earlier than October 1980, unless it was going to be 12 months earlier, and there was absolutely *no way* that was ever going to be possible. In a way, therefore, it was a self-imposing date'.

For the record, I should also make it clear that no one single decision was made to approve LC8 as it appeared in January 1978—large businesses do not operate like that, certainly not when they are controlled by the State! As far as the Government was concerned, the small car project had been in existence for a long time, and they were not in any mood for it to be rushed through. From the earliest days of the nationalised British Leyland concern, the Government and the National Enterprise Board, had been worried about labour relations in the Austin-Morris business, and repeatedly stated that they would rather cancel the project, and run down the Austin-Morris operation, than endure more industrial anarchy of the type suffered by the privately-owned British Leyland of the early 1970s.

As early as September 1976, when ADO88 was just getting into its stride, the company had sought commitment from the workforce, asking them to support the new project, and—more importantly—the new automated buildings and processes which would be needed to manufacture it. When the breakaway toolmakers' section of one union downed tools early in 1977, the NEB's reaction was to freeze all investment, and to defer approval for major building contracts to be signed. On March 2 1977, in fact, Eric Varley, the Industry Minister with responsibility for the NEB, went so far as to state to the House of Commons that there would be no further public money made available to British Leyland unless the strike ended, and five days later he also said that the 'Mini-replacement scheme' could be scrapped.

It was all part of a long drawn out process which finally convinced bloody-minded and perhaps politically-motivated union shop stewards and convenors that the potential supply of tax-payers' money to British Leyland was *not* limitless, and from this time a greater sense of reality began to take shape. Within two weeks this particular strike was over and, two months later, the NEB gave the formal go-ahead for the new small car.

Even in 1978, when Michael Edwardes' dynamic leadership had begun to take effect, it took time for all the hurdles to be cleared. The LC8 programme had been approved by the BL board of directors on Wednesday, January 11 1978, but it was not until June of that year that the Product Planning division was able to recommend a formal and detailed programme, derivatives, specifications, and all, to them. By mid-1978, in fact, LC8 had picked up a momentum all of its own and was coming to dominate the scene at Longbridge.

Chapter 5

Mighty Mini
A very public secret

Ideally, a new car should be developed in secret. Company salesmen hate to see existing models overshadowed by rumours of new ones and designers like to correct their mistakes in private. No team is perfect, and the minor disasters, or bright ideas and second thoughts, ought to occur behind closed doors, or high walls.

The LC8 project never stood a chance. Not only was it new, exciting and important, but it was also to come from a nationalised concern. Fleet Street, more than ever before, thought the public had a right to know about it, and never let management alone. Even under normal circumstances, security is one of the motor industry's biggest problems; concerns developing a new washing machine, or a new type of computer, have a much easier time. Most car makers have their own proving grounds, but in the end the new cars have to come out into the open, and be driven on public roads. At that point the vultures are ready to strike.

The new project had already sprung into the headlines in 1977 but, following the appointment of Michael Edwardes as chairman, and the publication of his plan to change the entire structure of the group, it moved even further into the public eye. This also coincided with a period in which the company's standing changed considerably. Post-Ryder, for the first two years at least, the public and the workforce had come to treat British Leyland as a typical, and conventional, nationalised concern. The workforce, in particular, seemed to decide that they were now guaranteed jobs for life, and acted accordingly. Productivity sagged, disputes became more frequent and management morale slumped alarmingly.

By 1977, when the damaging unofficial toolmakers' strike erupted, public opinion had turned against British Leyland. Trade Secretary Eric Varley had addressed 600 shop stewards on February 11, when it became clear that they would be rejecting a third year of pay restraint. Even though he pointed out that: 'For six of the last seven months, Leyland has been catastrophically affected by strikes, mostly internal', he was jeered and heckled. The outcome was that Roy Frazer, who led 6,000 toolmakers, demanded separate bargaining rights and began an indefinite strike from February 18.

Within days, 15,000 workers were laid off, and 11 plants were already idle. Within a week, that number had risen to 30,000, and only four of the Leyland Cars line up of 18 models were still being made. Eric Varley's threat to withhold investment was not new, as the *Daily Telegraph*'s leader column made clear: 'Threats to withdraw State investment funds unless performance improves are not believed by the workforce. Such threats have been made at regular intervals since

1975. Output per man, however, is now at 1969 levels . . .'.

In the end, it was not until the government gave British Leyland just 28 days to get back into full production, and to push this up to 20,000 cars a week, that the strike began to crumble. The fact that £200 million was due to be advanced in July 1977, and a further £200 million in the summer of 1978 to finance the development of new models, and that it was agreed that a total of almost a quarter of a million jobs, nationwide, would be lost if Leyland Cars was to close, made a difference. When it all came to an end on March 21 1977, more than 50,000 cars worth £100 million at retail values had been lost.

Right away, carefully engineered 'leaks' let it be known that new model strategy was being examined, as the *Daily Telegraph* pointed out: 'There are several formulae about eliminating models, but the planned Mini replacement is one candidate *that is likely to be scrapped if the Government cuts its share of investment.* [The italics are mine.] The cost of the Mini programme has soared from an estimated £100 million to £250 million'.

In the end, this particular course was not taken, and speculation about the future of Leyland Cars was rather swept aside by the sensational developments in September 1977, when Sir Richard Dobson felt obliged to resign as the group's chairman. A rather embarrassing hiatus developed when the Government searched around for a new chairman, and some of us (including the more cynical Fleet Street newspapers) gained the distinct impression that this was proving difficult. As my contemporary, Jeff Daniels, pointed out in his study of British Leyland models of the period:

'There was Sir Richard Dobson, after whose departure we gained the unfortunate impression that well-qualified people were queueing up not to take the task on. In the circumstances, it now seems surprising that a man of Michael Edwardes' qualities was persuaded into the chair. Historians, with the benefit of another ten years' hindsight, may mark the day of his appointment as the moment when the BL tide turned.'

Michael Edwardes—now Sir Michael, for his knighthood was bestowed in 1979— came to British Leyland on November 1 1977 with a daunting task to be tackled. A dimunitive South African of 47, with a degree in law, and most of his business experience with the Chloride group, Michael Edwardes had been that concern's chief executive since 1972. He took the chairmanship of British Leyland under a three-year contract, while retaining links with Chloride as its vice-chairman. Subsequently, that contract was extended and Sir Michael was due to leave BL in the autumn of 1982, by the time the first edition of this book is published. For the first time since nationalisation in 1975, the group was to have a chairman who was not only young, but an active industrialist, with a formidable and tough reputation.

He arrived at yet another critical point in British Leyland's history, for the company's annual pay round negotiations had just been completed. The award had been a 10 per cent increase, bitterly opposed by some factions because it was shaped according to government pay policy, and there had been threats of major strike action, parried by threats of break up, and sell up, British Leyland if the talks failed. The company's share of the UK car market, 31 per cent just pre-Ryder Report, and forecast to rise to 33 per cent in that over-optimistic document, had slumped to 20 per cent by October 1977.

When the doyen of Europe's motoring writers, Frenchman Edouard Seidler, interviewed Michael Edwardes in 1978, he pointed out that there had been 'lots of wishful thinking among Leyland's top management in the past', and hoped that the new management team was going to move away from this attitude.

It already had. In a whirlwind of activity occupying the winter of 1977/1978, Edwardes had re-jigged the group's structure, and confirmed its forward planning. The huge office block in Marylebone Road, London (ex-Castrol, who had moved out to Swindon) was vacated in favour of smaller premises in Piccadilly and Portman Square, and another big office block in Coventry (Leyland Coventry House) was also progressively run down.

Alex Park, British Leyland's chief executive from 1975 to 1977, became executive vice chairman, but resigned after only a month. Derek Whittaker, managing director, Leyland Cars, before Michael Edwardes arrived, saw that the cars group was to be broken up early in 1978, and also resigned. Early in 1978 the Austin-Morris group regained its identity, and Ray Horrocks, the 48-year-old ex-Ford 'whizz kid', responsible, among other things, for opening up the sporting Advanced Vehicle Operation, became its managing director. Jaguar-Rover-Triumph also re-emerged as a separate company, and it was not long before Jaguar was once again shaping its own destiny.

Right away, Michael Edwardes discovered how avidly the newspapers would fall upon any crumb of information which came from his offices, whether off the record or not. In one of his first briefings with motoring correspondents, he outlined confidential plans, which he hoped would remain confidential, and was rather taken aback by the detail which then appeared in print, notably in the *Sunday Telegraph* and the *Sunday Times*.

Kenneth Fleet, city editor of the *Sunday Times*, commented in January 1978 that: 'The post-Ryder period has seen very little new model development outside Rover and Jaguar and much more talk than action about a Super Mini', and at the same time reported rumours that up to 30,000 workers (one in four of the entire labour force) would have to be axed from the cars divisions.

One massively detailed feature in the financial pages of the *Sunday Times* summed up what was being planned, or at least what was being rumoured. Published on January 8 1978, it was so factual, and so circumstantial, that it could only have been prepared with the aid of the public relations staff of the new companies. In general terms, it stated that when Michael Edwardes arrived to take control, on November 1 1977, British Leyland had far too many different factories—in fact the Leyland Cars group had no fewer than 29 separate plants. £42 million had already been spent on 'the new Mini', which was to be redesigned yet again, and £300 millions was now quoted as the investment needed for this model. The LC10 range, a larger design intended to take over from the Austin Maxi, the Austin Allegro and the Triumph Dolomite, was also mentioned (possibly for the first time in public?), and the suggestion was made that: 'many motor experts think it should take precedence over the Mini'.

The greatest possible attention, however, was given to the small car project, known to have come in for reworking during the winter, and these were the actual words used: 'But everything palls before the dilemma about the future of ADO88 . . . The Ryder Report pressed Leyland to accelerate the Mini programme . . . Critics said that Leyland could never achieve the economics of scale necessary to compete with the new generation of Super Minis launched by Fiat, Renault, Ford, Vauxhall, and now Chrysler. Leyland would need to make about 350,000 Minis a year—about half of its existing output—and even this was a bare minimum.

'Several motor-watchers, including some former senior Leyland men, thought

Edwardes was planning to chop the Mini replacement altogether . . . Instead, he is keeping both the old Mini, and the plan for a new car that will hopefully meet the European Super Mini competition head on.'

By this stage the new car was still not officially being called LC8 in public (that came later), but Michael Edwardes and his colleagues had begun referring to the 'Mighty Mini'. Until mid-1979, when the name Metro would finally be adopted, it was 'Mighty Mini' as far as the public were concerned.

This sort of detail scrutiny was typical of the way the car had to be developed, and prepared for production, in the months to come, and there is no doubt that it made a difficult task even more taxing. However, even though the press soon began to warm to the pugnacious Edwardes, and his equally determined lieutenants, Ray Horrocks and Harold Musgrove, not everyone was in favour. The industrial climate at Longbridge was still not restful, for the leader of the union shop stewards, Derek Robinson, was entirely opposed to the new schemes: 'Given the support we expect from factory meetings', Robinson stated, 'we will be telling him we are not accepting his decisions'.

Such remarks made in years gone by would have worried Leyland management considerably. The new team, knowing full well that government support could now be cut off at very short notice, were not disposed to take threats of industrial action too seriously, and pressed on. Major moves were still discussed with the trade unions, but policy decisions were rarely affected by the more Luddite attitudes.

By the spring of 1978, BL Cars Ltd, which had taken over from Leyland Cars, had completed its five-year forward programme, and had submitted it to the National Enterprise Board for approval. It was not for some time that details became public, but it was always apparent that it would feature what came to be known as 'product led recovery'. Leyland Cars had, indeed, let its new-model programme slip back, and BL Cars was out to reverse the process. At least one major new model every year, was the aim, and in the years which have passed since then, no target has been missed, and no major project abandoned. The 'Mighty Mini'—LC8, as it had now become—was scheduled for launch in the autumn of 1980, but before this there was to be the V8-engined Land-Rover, the Series III Jaguar range, and the Morris Ital, though the idea of building a 2 + 2 coupé version of the TR7 sports car had already been dropped when the closure of the Speke (Liverpool) factory had been announced. At this point, too, liaison with Honda had not been established, and industry rumour was that there might eventually be some kind of joint project with Renault instead.

Even so, it was all rather distressingly public, and major rivals like Ford must have been gleeful at the amount of information their forward planners were able to glean. Michael Edwardes didn't like it one bit, but knew that as the chairman of a publically-owned enterprise he had little choice in the matter. In March 1978, however, he appealed not only for the £200 million of investment capital, as planned, but for the Government not to keep questioning investment programmes every three months or so. He asked that there should be no Government interference in the investment programme and confirmed that he wanted to see the workforce in BL Cars reduced by 12,500 'by natural wastage', with about 2,000 of those jobs going from Longbridge. I should make it clear, at this point, that there had been virtually no slimming down under the 'Ryder Report' management—instead, in 1976, the company had even been actively recruiting when it seemed that the market share was at last on the increase.

By the autumn of 1978, with the LC8 programme going ahead at full blast, and with the rebuilding of Longbridge now obvious to anyone who passed the gates, and to every worker on the ground, the Edwardes regime had properly established itself. The group as a whole was just, but only just, making an operating profit, but Austin-Morris was a big loss-maker and, as the need for heavy investment built up, it was quite obvious that there would be huge losses in the next few years.

Although the company eventually settled with the workforce on a five per cent pay increase for 1979 (which was in line with government guide lines—even though many other concerns were not able to settle for similar low figures), achieved their first common wage review date in every factory, and made their first moves towards wage parity in different locations, there were still major difficulties with the Austin-Morris workforce.

As Michael Edwardes said in his interview with Edouard Seidler, published in *Autocar* in November 1978: 'When 95 per cent of the workforce want to work, and five per cent do not, there is too little democracy if it is the five per cent who get their way. What is missing is discipline, both by management and by the unions'. The problem, however, was not at national level, where union leaders understood the grave financial state of BL, even if they were not happy to negotiate with a realistic eye to that fact, but at plant level. The union shop stewards, led by the self-confessed Communist sympathiser, convenor Derek Robinson, did not accept that one way to underpin the future was not only to accept the new technology proposed for Metro production, but the lower manning levels involved. Instead, they publically opposed the 'Edwardes Recovery Plan'.

Time after time in recent years, the workforce had been summoned to the green hill of Cofton Park, across the road from the main Longbridge assembly buildings, and time after time they had accepted their stewards' advice—which was usually to reject the latest management plan or wage offer. During 1979 however, their mood had gradually been changing. When Derek Robinson came out with his opposition to the Edwardes Recovery Plan, and urged the workforce actively to oppose it, BL management immediately sacked him. Strike action was called for to demand his reinstatement, but when management showed no signs of retracting from their decision (Edwardes even threatened to begin closing down the Austin-Morris business if the workforce did not accept his proposals), the mood changed abruptly. In February 1980, at a mass meeting in Cofton Park, Robinson's pleas were overwhelmingly rejected. One placard, held up by a Longbridge worker, said it all: 'On your bike, Red Robbo'. From that moment, it seemed, sanity returned to Longbridge and morale began to improve.

In the meantime, the designers and development engineers had been working away at the new model. Even though ADO88 was now officially dead, there was never any question of scrapping the prototypes already built. Ten Semi-Engineered Prototypes (SEPs) had been made in 1975/1976, and no fewer than 24 Fully-Engineered Prototypes (FEPs) had followed them in 1977, the very first being completed in July. It was going to take at least a year before cars looking correct, and like the approved LC8 in every detail, would be available, so most of the testing would have to be carried out on ADO88s, even though they were different in so many ways.

The engineers, however, found much merit in this, as Fred Coultas explained: 'Naturally we carried on using ADO88 prototypes for some time. In fact it was very useful to us—all clouds are not grey all the time. Once the big decision had been made, it meant that the security wraps could come off ADO88, and we could fool all the spies . . .'.

This, of course, explains why almost all the 'sneak preview' pictures of the 'Mighty Mini' were treated very casually by BL public relations staff—quite simply because they were usually of ADO88 FEPs, which looked entirely different in detail from the LC8 itself.

The FEPs had been built in a batch, with pressed body panels produced on what is known in the industry as 'soft' tooling, where the die material is Kirksite, one which is easily formed, but which usually begins to distort after about 25 panel sets have been produced.

Until 1978, every ADO88 sent out on test had had to carry disguise, to keep its full shape a secret from prying eyes. At this time, too, British Leyland had no proving ground of their own (unlike the other members of the 'Big Four'—Ford, Chrysler UK and Vauxhall), so testing had to be carried out either on the public highways, or at the industry's communal, and none-too-secure, proving ground, MIRA, near Nuneaton.

There were generally two ways of achieving disguise. Prototypes would be built up as normal, with every available piece of skin panelling and glass in place, after which the 'make-up' would be applied. Some cars were treated to a time-consuming and

To run secret cars on public roads, you need to disguise them. This was an early production Metro, heavily obscured by the false bonnet and grille layout and by the canvas 'tilt' over the tail.

detailed counterfeiting job, where extra cardboard or glass-fibre shapes were fixed into place. Some ADO88s had their bonnets built up to look less wedge-nose than they should have been, some had 'bustles' added to their tails to disguise the shape and even the existence of the hatchback, and some had camouflage panelling added over the side windows to break up their true profile—some had the whole treatment applied, and the result was quite grotesque. The shape of the disguised cars fooled no one into thinking that *this* was what would eventually be out on sale—but at least it kept the competition guessing about the real shapes hidden away underneath.

Another way was perhaps not to disguise the front of the car too severely, but to obliterate the shape behind the front doors by adding what is known in the trade as a canvas 'tilt'. At first glance, therefore, such a prototype would look like a small pick-up, or commercial vehicle. Development teams who really got into the swing of things made sure that their prototypes were painted in drab colours—battleship grey, dark green, or unpolished chassis black are favourites—and if their cars are registered they make sure that numbers are not taken out locally. It used to be said once that BL prototypes were registered (but not seen!) in Essex, which is the home of Ford, and that Ford used to return the compliment by registering *their* cars in the West Midlands.

The problem in 1977 and 1978, however, was not only that these cars had to venture out on to the roads, but that the work they carried out could not always be conclusive. Fred Coultas again: 'It's very difficult to carry out all the tests we need to

Crashing a Metro prototype against the concrete barrier at MIRA to ensure that it has a strong and safe body shell.

do right away on a camouflaged vehicle—I'm referring to cooling work, performance testing, heater development, and checking out the aerodynamics.'

It was obvious that the aerodynamics of the finished vehicle would be affected by the disguise, and although the initial acceleration would be unaffected by cardboard or glass fibre hang-ons, the high-speed acceleration would suffer considerably. There were questions of external and internal air flow to be investigated, the position of intake and outlet grilles, heater flow through the car, the layout and performance of windscreen wiper and rear screen wipe/wash equipment, the establishment of maximum speed, the checking out of fuel economy under all conditions, and it was also necessary to make sure that no exhaust fumes were being drawn in through the seals of the hatchback, nor that road filth would tend to obscure the rear lamps, or the rear window itself.

The engineers, however, had little choice but to battle on at first, and the decision to throw away the disguise after LC8 had been chosen instead of ADO88 was a great relief. Until then, all testing of 'clean' ADO88s had been carried out at night, on proving grounds lent by sympathetic suppliers like Lucas and Automotive Products (one near Coventry, the other near Banbury), or overseas. For a time it was normal to see large lorries sweeping out of Longbridge, looking furtive and anonymous. Inside, one or more ADO88s would be on their way to yet another testing assignment.

Engineers in large companies often admit to having been to far-off countries with test cars, but this is rarely done with a holiday, or free transport, in mind. ADO88s were taken to Finland or to Canada in search of really cold conditions (Canada, I learned, is a much 'drier' cold than Finland, and more predictably cold, at that), to the German autobahns for flat-out endurance testing, where there are no speed limits, and to the shimmeringly arid autostradas of southern Italy for assessment of everything from the ventilation to the engine's durability in very hot conditions. Expeditions were also made to East Africa, Australia and other territories where the new car might eventually be sold.

Like all other major concerns, BL are not too proud to study cars built by their competitors. In readiness for ADO88 work, two VW Polos, a Renault 5, a Fiat 127, a Peugeot 104 and a Vauxhall Chevette were all drafted into Longbridge for assessment, and comparison. One engineer, who had better remain anonymous, also told me: 'Ford's Fiesta hadn't been announced at that stage, but we got one from Germany as soon as possible in 1976. Then we heaved a sigh of relief . . .'. Most of these comparator cars were used for at least 30,000 miles, often as 'chase' cars for ADO88s or LC8s on test, or for driving by management. Was it predictable that the most conventionally-engineered of them all, the Vauxhall Chevette, gave the least trouble?

Wind tunnel testing of body styles had begun in 1975, well before there was a complete car to test. Even though the price of petrol was still down at about 75 pence a gallon, the impact of the Energy Crisis of 1973/1974 was still fresh in the minds of the designers, and every effort was to be made to smooth the shape of the new car. Although BL do not have their own wind tunnel, they had easy access to the full-size MIRA facility at Nuneaton, and were even allowed to use the Fiat tunnel in Turin, where there was apparently no problem with security.

Although drag figures are only relative (the results for one car can vary from place to place—even, as one industry cynic told me, from week to week), the Metro story starts with the fact that the drag coefficient of the bluff-nosed Mini Clubman was

0.54, a poor figure by 1980s standards. The very first ADO88 mock-up, a full-size glass-fibre model from the styling studios, recorded 0.44, which was something of a disappointment, but at least it gave the aerodynamicists a challenge. Time was short, and there was also a minor conflict between low-drag requirements, the 'clear rear screen' situation in heavy rain, and the position of the exhaust pipe outlet, but by a whole series of minor changes, not least to the rear roof 'flip-up', and the shape of the body sills, the drag coefficient was coaxed down to the final figure of 0.412.

Nowadays, where every little bit of fuel economy becomes an extra selling point, gains of 0.005 in the drag coefficient are worth having, which explains why so much attention is now paid to the shape and location of the compulsory rear view mirrors on the doors, and why the spoiler on the roof and down the sides of the MG Metro's hatchback is so carefully shaped. On the original ADO88 glass-fibre models, and on the early prototypes, there was no front spoiler under the front bumper, but this has always been a feature of LC8 Metros.

There is nothing very glamorous or scientific about wind tunnel testing—not yet, at least. Every engineer knows how some previous cars have been better than expected, and some worse—none of them, and not even the cleverest computer, can forecast how a new model will perform. With the Metro project, as with others before it, some unfortunate conscript had to stand around in the howling gale of the full size tunnel, muffled up to the eyebrows and trying to look cheerful about it, moving a 'smoke-gun' from one point in the air stream to another. Like most development jobs in the industry, the inspiration makes up five per cent of the total, but the perspiration (or a streaming cold!) accounts for the rest.

Many hours, for instance, were spent in refining the shape of the front grille, and the headlamps which flank it. 'But you've got a *total* conflict there', Fred Coultas says, 'for one the one hand you'd like all the air to go up and over the nose, to keep the flow smooth, and on the other hand you've got to cool the radiator somehow!'

According to the programme, it was all meant to be routine—but the fates soon put paid to that. One evening in October 1978, just as staff and technicians were packing up to go home, the alarm was raised—there was a fire, and precious prototypes and materials were involved! The cause was electrical, and the location was one of the tunnels under Longbridge. It took time to get fire-fighting equipment to the area, and by the time the blaze was put out, no fewer than four ADO88 prototypes had been damaged.

For many years, the tunnels of Longbridge were little known. Some were originally air-raid shelters, some were for transport of materials and components, some were later used for storage. There were even tunnels into which rejected prototypes, one-offs, and engineers' crazy schemes were locked away. By the 1970s, some were used for garaging new models between their turns of duty. It was one of these whose electrical wiring finally shorted out, and consumed thousands of hours of hard work in minutes.

The toll was depressing. One FEP—the fifth such ADO88—was lost altogether, while three other cars, SEP7, SEP10 and FEP8 were all badly damaged. To look back at test records is to see just how much disruption was caused—six months work on fuel economy and exhaust emission testing, two months on braking development, and other depressing statistics. Not that there was any spare time for recriminations. Work had to go on, and the deadlines were not allowed to slip.

But it wasn't all bad news. 'Early on, we were very puzzled by the results of a barrier crash test', Fred Coultas recalls. 'When we slung a body shell into the block

At Thatcham, BL engineers see a Cortina crashed deliberately into the rear quarter of a Metro, then assess the damage, and see how repair costs can be minimised.

at 30 mph, the steering column only came back about three quarters of an inch. Since the regulations allow us up to five inches, we were a bit worried. Had we over-engineered something, or was it a 'rogue' test? But when we repeated the test, the result was nearly as good. The column was pushed *up* and back, but never by more than 1.5 inches; we were very pleased by that.'

By 1979, all the doubts about the ADO88, and the delays caused by the restyle, and the birth of LC8, had been forgotten. The 'Mighty Mini' project was rapidly becoming the biggest ever tackled at Longbridge. Certainly it was going to be the longest—six years from the original clay styles of 1974 to the start-up of series production—and it was already breaking all records for the cost of development and the investment needed.

The numbers began to accelerate away from anything previously experienced. The surviving ADO88s—more than 20 were still in use at the end of 1978—were about to be joined by 10 Fully-Engineering Prototypes (FEP) LC8s to the finalised body style, and another 40 PRVs (Proving Vehicles) were expected in the summer, when the first 'off-tools' body shells had been built. In spite of the fire, no target dates were missed. The record shows that the first FEP ran in January, and that the proving vehicles were delivered on time. ('I know it sounds Irish', one engineer told me, 'but the first FEP to run was actually the second to be built . . . .')

Background photograph *Check wind tunnel testing, using localised smoke generators, to make sure that the production car behaves in the same way as the first fibreglass models.* **Inset** *MIRA's dust tunnel seeks out every nook and cranny in a new car's body shell, for leaks. On this Metro FEP car, there were very few.*

In the meantime, BL Cars was well on its way to acquiring a proving ground at last. Way back in the heady days of 1975, when the Ryder Report foresaw expanding sales, and increased profits by the end of the 1970s, there had been talk of a new design centre close to the M42 motorway at Dorridge, and of a vast new proving ground to go with it. This scheme collapsed as the company's sales plunged, and a low-budget solution had to be found.

Newspaper rumours not only suggested that BL Cars would buy Chrysler's proving ground at Bruntingthorpe airfield, near Lutterworth, but (even less likely, this one) that they would take over the MIRA proving ground near Nuneaton, and dispossess dozens of other firms which already rented the facilities from time to time. The truth was more mundane.

BL needed a large proving ground, and they wanted it to be in the Midlands, close to the Longbridge, Solihull, Canley and Browns Lane factories. Politics, financial realities and expediency meant that only one type of site was practical—like those used by BL's major competition (except Vauxhall), it would have to be a converted airfield.

The ideal site was found at Gaydon, close to the Warwick–Banbury main road, an ex-strike Command base which had once been the home of a V-bomber squadron, but which was now only on the RAF's 'care and maintenance' roster. Gaydon covered a large area, already had a two-mile main runway, and was almost entirely flat. By 1977 conversion work had begun, by the end of 1978 the first facilities were available, and during 1979 the new proving ground, controlled by a new BL offshoot—BL Technology—was fully commissioned.

Almost at once the pace of development was stepped up. Even though MIRA's major facilities—the pavé track, the barrier crash facilities, and the wind tunnel—were still important to LC8, a lot of the work could be carried out in complete secrecy at Gaydon. BL's own figures tell their own story—in the first three years a quarter of a million miles of durability testing had been built up on ADO88s, but by the time Metro was announced in October 1980, that figure had rushed up to two million and more. The use of more prototypes and more men had helped, but Gaydon had helped even more.

Security-conscious managers could now breathe freely again. Not only were most of the cars used still ADO88s, whose style was obsolete, but there was now no danger of prying eyes looking over the cars at an industry proving ground. At Gaydon, one immediate feature was a vast earth bank thrown up by the contractors to screen secret cars from passing motorists on the A41 main road.

Some news hounds, however, were not easily put off. With patience, it was possible to stake out the recognised 'cold-climate' locations of Finland or Canada (shamefaced BL engineers once admitted that they arrived at one particular site to find teams from VW and Daimler-Benz already in residence, doing similar work), and by resigning oneself to many hours of boring waiting there was always a chance that an undisguised car might be seen slipping in or out of the gates at Longbridge.

Car, the British monthly magazine, was determined to get its scoop, and finally splashed pictures of the new car all over the cover of its July 1979 issue, with a spread of further pictures inside. 'From the crude prototype we pictured in *Car*, November 1978', they trumpeted, 'development models have evolved into far more complete vehicles, only partially disguised, and fully equipped.' The problem for *Car*, as so often in these features, was that they had got it all wrong. The car they snapped was an early ADO88—an SEP, in fact—already two years old and visually quite obsolete!

Much of their commentary was broadly accurate, but there were serious errors which convulsed BL's PR staff and engineers when they read the piece. Apart from commenting on the style, *Car* suggested not only that the transverse engines would be tilted substantially rearwards, but that they had aluminium cylinder heads with overhead camshaft operation. They also suggested that a three-cylinder engine might be offered as an option. *Car*'s sneak pictures were sold to other magazines and newspapers, and even appeared on television. At the time, no one could quite understand why BL's staff took it all with such equanimity. Now, perhaps, they do.

In the meantime, BL as a whole had been making a lot of headlines. In spite of losing £300 million worth of cars in strikes, BL Cars had swung from a £32 million trading loss to a profit of £20 million in 1978. The price of petrol in Britain at last broke through the £1 per gallon barrier, as crude oil prices began to soar all over the world, and this immediately increased the demand for Minis, and made prospects for the LC8 even more promising than before.

The biggest headlines of all, however, came as rumours began to spread of a proposed BL-Honda tie-up for the early 1980s, and for a time the LC8 project was even pushed into the background. It took time for the rumours to crystallise into actual hard news but, by the autumn, it was clear that LC8 was likely to be followed by a British-built Triumph-badged Honda, and that LC10 was likely to slip even further back into the early 1980s.

In April and May of 1979, all this was swept aside when BL decided to make the naming of the LC8 a worker-participation exercise. It would have been easy to go through the long drawn-out process of vetting names, taking opinion from managers, directors and the sales force, and making sure the name was acceptable in all possible territories, but Sir Michael Edwardes and Ray Horrocks judged, rightly as it transpired, that to ask the workforce finally to choose the name would be a publicity-conscious way of doing it.

The idea itself had originated through the Austin-Morris 'suggestion box' scheme in July 1977, but at the time it had been thought premature. By the beginning of 1979 Ray Horrocks had received an internal memo listing 38 names, many of which had been provided by Novamark, an organisation specialising in this activity. Among the names were Brava, Monte, Riva, Milo, Match, Midas and Monte—three of which, Match, Riva and Monde, being considered particularly strong. In this list two names—Metro and Maestro—were conspicuous by their absence.

Austin-Morris finally put out a special four-page edition of the works newspaper, called the 'Austin-Morris Express Special', inviting the workforce to choose a name. One page explained why certain names could not be used because of trade mark difficulties, or because they had unfortunately meanings in some foreign languages, and went on: 'In the summer of 1978, Austin-Morris marketing staffs began a mammoth task, in assembling a shopping list of possible names . . . New names and old names, long name and short names, no holds were barred. You name it, they listed it. The list reached a grand total of 8,500 potential names. 22 major territories around the world were pinpointed as proposed markets for the new car . . .'.

The whole of the back page was effectively a voting slip. Each worker was asked to choose one of the final three titles which had been chosen. Did he prefer Metro, Maestro or Match? More than 37,000 were eligible to vote. 19,781 workers—assembly men, staff, managers, even directors—53 per cent of the total, returned

voting slips by May 11. The result was close, for votes were cast as follows: Mini
Metro—8,599 votes; Mini Maestro—8,332 votes; Mini Match—2,793 votes.

While all this was going on, and before BL announced the choice of Metro on May
23 1979, the local newspaper, the *Birmingham Evening Mail*, polled their readers,
who plumped for 'Maestro', a name known to have been favoured by some Austin-
Morris executives.

So, Metro it was, by a narrow margin. More than 65 per cent of the Longbridge
workers had troubled to vote, for at the end of the day there was going to be a further
inducement. As the company newspaper put it: 'Arrangements are now being made
for a draw in June of all entries made voting for the chosen name. There will be two
winners—one from Longbridge, and one from Austin-Morris employees at other
locations—the prize in each case being one of the very first Metros to be produced.'

BL supporters, or critics, had also been making their own suggestions, and Sir
Michael Edwardes' office received a steady flow of bright ideas. In March 1979,
before the poll had been announced, Mr J.P. Hall from Slough had suggested
'Boopsie', which caused consternation until it was pointed out that it was a Greek
dimunitive meaning 'baby'. A Mr Robinson suggested MiniMacro, or MacroMini,
which had its charm, but Ms Amanda Jane Sinclair of Crowborough in Sussex was
so sure that she had hit on the right title, seven months after the pool result had been
announced that she suggested to Sir Michael. 'I have thought of a name for your new
Mini, which will be an absolute winner. I am so certain that I think it is worth a Mini
in exchange! If you should decide to use it, it far surpasses Metro, and I am
absolutely certain it will make an impact.' Her offer was not taken up, and the name
was not revealed.

Like Ford with the Fiesta (who had to gain permission from General Motors to use
the name, for it was one of GM's trade marks), BL were not entirely free to use the
name Metro. In Birmingham, just a few miles from the Longbridge factory, the long-
established company of Metro-Cammell was still building tube trains and other
railway rolling stock very successfully, and their agreement had to be gained to allow
'Metro' to appear on a car. It was not felt, however, that anyone would confuse a
wedge-nosed mini-car with a 1980s-style tube train.

In the meantime, the marketing research department had thought it necessary to
conduct another clinic, if only to reassure themselves that decisions taken at the end
of 1977 were still valid. In every way this expedition to Blackpool, on June 7 1979,
was an occasion for stiff upper lips and crossed fingers, for it was now far too late to
consider making any style changes without incurring horrendous delays and extra
costs. The chosen model was not a complete prototype, but a fully-detailed glass-fibre
styling mock-up, complete with the latest interior and equipment; painted white, as
always on these occasions, it was wheeled into a large hall, to be judged alongside
four competitive 'Superminis' which included a standard Mini, a Ford Fiesta, and the
VW Polo.

450 motorists had been invited on this occasion, and it was gratifying to discover
that most of them liked the Metro very much indeed. The aerodynamic lines, the
'package', and the versatile seating layout all came in for praise and there was little,
apart from some criticism of trim colour and design, to cause second (or final)
thoughts.

Marketing research, however, were intrigued to find that some motorists still
preferred the 20-year-old Mini as their first choice, and it also proved that some
motorists were not at all perceptive about their own cars if the clinic example was not

coloured up and badged completely. As the clinic report pointed out: 'One lady, for example, criticised at length the exterior style of one car when she in fact had bought the same model only six months previously!'

There was one repercussion of the Blackpool clinic, the type of 'leak' which obsesses staff dealing with this sort of exercise. In spite of pleas to keep confidential everything which had been noted inside the conference hall, one motorist went home to talk to his local newspaper correspondent, and the result was that a very revealing artist's impression of LC8, the definitive Metro, appeared in the *West Lancs Evening Gazette* on June 22 1979.

Two years earlier, this might have caused knees to quake in the corridors of power at Longbridge, but not any more. In those two years, a remarkable turn-round in company morale and outlook, had been achieved. The BL Group, as a whole, was still a big loss maker (in spite of chalking up another trading profit in the first half of 1979), but everyone in the know could now sense the impact which the new Metro was going to make in 1980. At Longbridge, the evidence of change was all around them, and at BL in general the workforce was gradually being slimmed down to take account of the realities of the 1980s. Perhaps the change of government, following the general election of 1979, had nothing to do with it, but the settlement of another modest wage round, without strife, in the autumn of 1979, most certainly had.

In the summer of 1979, personnel changes came thick and fast, as Mark Snowdon moved up from his Product Planning directorship to control the destiny of all product development at Austin-Morris, while Ray Horrocks moved up from Austin-Morris to become managing director of the entire cars group. The dynamic Harold Musgrove, a born-again Brummie whose incisive and sometimes abrasive manner was instantly recognised by anyone on the assembly lines, took his place.

It was Musgrove, the son of a Leyland tradesman, the ex-Longbridge apprentice, now the production engineering director, who had had the job of turning a Metro dream into reality. It was Musgrove who once said to Brian James of the *Daily Mail*: 'I used to take this car into a room and sit with it for an hour. On my own. Just staring at it . . . asking "could I really *love* something like you?" ' It was also Musgrove, whose golf handicap suffered so badly in the Metro years that he reckoned he would need a caddy to show him round the course next time he visited it. It was Musgrove who became the most enthusiastic backer of the Metro project—and its fiercest critic. It was Musgrove who was Austin-Morris' front man when Metro was being launched, and who revelled in it.

He could not have been appointed at a more critical moment. The time for designing and developing the Metro was nearly over. The time to start building cars was just about to begin.

Chapter 6

Rebuilding for robots
The reshaping of Longbridge

When Harold Musgrove and Tony Gilroy read this chapter, I hope they will understand. When I talked to them, they assured me that the new welding robots, and the automatic processes which went with them, were only one small part of the Metro story—but they also agreed that the robots were making most headlines. In fact, if ever there was a way of glamorising the massive change in bricks and mortar, in equipment, and in productivity, which went into the rebuilding of Longbridge, this was it.

The problem for me, as a motoring enthusiast, is that although it is easy enough to enthuse over the romantic launching of a new car—particularly one so important and charismatic as the Metro—there is really nothing glamorous about the building of a new factory. Even so, Tony Gilroy, who became Operations Director at Longbridge in 1978, when the huge operation had got under way, puts it very succinctly in one sentence: 'We had to replace technology that was 40 years out of date, with the technology of the future'.

He also told me that this was no ordinary project, no routine re-shaping of production lines to make way for a new model, but it was a fundamentally different approach to the building of a new car. It's easy to talk about robots, about computers, and about mechanised manufacture, but in the case of the Metro the entire method of making the car, of motivating the workforce, and of ensuring high quality standards, was going to be different. After 75 gradual and progressive years at Longbridge, it amounted to an entirely new start.

I ought to spend time relating what had happened at Longbridge, and to the entire Austin-Morris manufacturing complex (the old BMC business, in fact) in the years which led up to the birth of the Metro. When Austin and Nuffield merged in 1952, to form the British Motor Corporation, their main motor car assembly factories were at Longbridge, a few miles south of the centre of Birmingham, and at Cowley, just to the east of Oxford. Apart from the new Car Assembly Building No 1 at Longbridge, a visionary brain-child of Leonard Lord, both were old, sprawling, and a real hotch-potch of buildings and facilities.

Industrial archaeology is all very well, just so long as one doesn't have to build modern products therein—and in the case of the Longbridge and Cowley sites, there was a considerable amount of history to be observed. The first Austin car was built at Longbridge in 1906, in buildings originally erected in 1892 on a 2½ acre site, with a frontage on to the Bristol road of a mere 200 feet. The first Morris car, assembled at Cowley, took shape in a building last used as a military training college, but originally

Top *Laboratory testing of a new Metro, in this case with the analysis of noise in mind.*

Above *Autocar's 5,000-miles-in-five-days Metro at rest, very briefly, outside the Coliseum, in Rome.*

Right *With 4,800 of its scheduled 5,000-miles-in-five days run complete, the Metro (author at the wheel) poses briefly near the Atomium in Brussels.*

Left *Richard Longman in one of the brightly liveried 'Datapost' Metros which competed in the RAC British Saloon Car Championship.* **Below left** *The Frazer Tickford is actually a considerably modified Metro 1.3S, with coachwork by Tickford, who have long-established links with Aston-Martin-Lagonda.* **Below** *The Metro sectioned, showing the ingenious 'packaging' which went into the little car.*

Metro

Distinctive styling touches identify the MG Metro 1300, launched in May 1982.

The horseshoe-shaped rear spoiler of the MG Metro is not only a recognition point, but it reduces aerodynamic drag by five per cent.

Under the bonnet, the MG Metro looks the same as other Metros except for the light alloy rocker cover—there's more power there too!

The MG Metro 'office' with superb sports seats, specially-styled instruments and a padded-rimmed steering wheel.

erected as a grammar school in the mid-19th century—indeed, when William Morris bought the buildings, they had been disused for 21 years!

In both cases, expansion had been gradual, and carried out on an *ad hoc* basis. Austin's big body-making factory, West Works, had been built before the *First World War*, and even by 1920 the factories covered more than 100 acres. More and more buildings grew up in the 1920s and 1930s, followed by a Government-financed 'shadow factory' during the Hitler war. It was not until the late 1940s, however, that Leonard Lord decided to build new assembly facilities on what was still known as the aerodrome to the south of the old 100 acre complex. CAB1 was

Harold Musgrove, who became chairman and managing director of Austin-Morris in 1980. His was the major responsibility for bringing the rebuilding of Longbridge to a successful conclusion and ushering the Metro into production.

finished in 1951 and CAB2 (to the east of it), came on stream in 1962.

The Morris factories gradually extended themselves further and further south-east along the Cowley road and, by the end of the 1930s, they were almost reaching the boundary of the Pressed Steel Co's body assembly factory. All the Morris (Nuffield, actually) expansion in the 1940s and 1950s was on the other (south) side of the main road, and an overhead conveyor was built to connect the older assembly complex to the Pressed Steel buildings.

During the 16-year life of BMC, little attempt was made to modernise these rambling factories. All priorities were given to the design of new engines and new cars, to a badge-engineering programme which saw MG, Riley and Wolseley badges appearing on the most unlikely models, and to attempts to give BMC an 'advanced engineering' image. The two main sources of car production, Cowley and Longbridge, continued to build cars in their own distinctive manner. Cowley relied almost entirely on supplies of bodies, engines and transmissions from satellite factories many miles away—all its engines, for instance, came from Coventry, 60 miles distant. Longbridge, at least, built *some* of its engines, *some* of its transmissions, and *some* of its bodies 'in-house'. Even so, it was still something of a fragmented operation.

Before British Leyland was formed in 1968 (and, indeed, for some years after-wards), it was possible to see bodies, mechanical supplies, even complete motor cars, being transported in both directions, up and down the main Oxford–Coventry and Oxford–Birmingham highways. It made little economic sense, especially in terms of transport costs.

Under British Leyland, at least, a start was made, but at first almost all the money was spent at Cowley, which needed it most. The Austin Maxi of 1969 came first, then the Morris Marina of 1971, and finally the Princess 18/22 range of 1975. While all this was going on, the Mini continued to be the dominant model at Longbridge, though the 1100s and 1300s sold very strongly until replaced by the Austin Allegro in 1973, as did the Austin/Morris/Wolseley 1800/2200 front-wheel-drive saloons until discontinued at the beginning of 1975.

The big questions to be settled in 1975, when the company had just come under Government control, and while ADO88 was finally taking shape, were how much investment capital could be needed, and where the cars should actually be put together? Both questions, in fact, were heavily dependent on the design of the car, and on the layout of major components going into it.

I ought to make it clear that it was not Michael Edwardes' team, nor even that of Alex Park and Derek Whittaker, who decided to make the hugely expensive leap into the technology of the 1980s. To their credit (for both, in the years which followed nationalisation, were much-maligned men), it was Lord Stokes and his lieutenant, John Barber, who made that decision. Even though they ultimately lost the battle to control the company's finances, it should never be forgotten that they originated the bare bones of the ADO88 project, and decreed the way in which it was to be built, in 1974.

Cowley, Longbridge, or a completely new 'greenfield' site? That was the intriguing conundrum facing the company in 1974, when its future looked promising. There were no other sensible possibilities. Other volume-production factories in the group—at Canley (Coventry), Solihull, and Speke (Liverpool)—all promised to have busy and exciting futures ahead of them. Isn't it ironic, now, that the assembly halls at each of these plants have all now been closed down for lack of business?

In the end, the problem was almost solved automatically. As soon as the nationalised concern started to operate in 1975, it became clear that further factory expansion was out of the question, so all thoughts of a new 'greenfield' site were abandoned. (No sites, incidentally, had even been pinpointed at the time). Cowley lost out for two very basic reasons—in 1975 it was intended to make ADO88 a direct replacement for the Mini, which was only being built at Longbridge, and the engines and transmissions intended for ADO88 were also being planned for production in the existing Longbridge factory as well. Cowley, it was hoped, would be busy for years to come with the assembly of Marinas, Maxis and Princesses, and there was no space to add another model to that line-up. The new mini car, therefore, would have to find a home at Longbridge.

But what sort of a home? In whatever form it took the project was always going to be very costly. When the previous project, ADO74, had been cancelled in 1974, it had been costed out at £130 million, though this assumed a new engine and gearbox under a conventionally-engineered body shell. ADO88, the ancestor of the Metro, was going to be very different, and more costly still—its engine/gearbox unit was going to be the same, in general layout, as the Mini and Allegro, but its body engineering was not. Quite soon, it seemed, figures in excess of £200 millions were being bandied about, and many politicians were openly horrified at the prospect. This figure, incidentally, had been included in the £1,264 millions promised by the Ryder Report of 1975, one which had largely been inspired by the long-term projections developed for Lord Stokes immediately before the crash.

The big change intended for the new car was not in its engine, or in its suspension, but in the way the body shell was to be put together. It was to be nothing less than a revolution in methods at Longbridge—one which would make Metro the most efficiently-built car in the world. The system previously used at Longbridge had developed only slowly, and gradually, in the post-war years and was really little more modern than that first used at the end of the Second World War. Bodies were assembled, jig-saw fashion, by being clamped into simple jigs, and by being spot-welded or gas-welded together by hardworking men armed with single guns or torches. In more than 30 years at post-war Longbridge, only the shapes, and the varieties of body, had changed. For Metro, a real revolution was planned. For Metro, although it would be impossible to eliminate manual labour, and handwork, altogether, machines could be designed—*would* be designed—to take all the drudgery out of the job. It would need equipment and processes entirely new to Britain, and it was going to be an enormous challenge.

Tony Gilroy puts it all into perspective: 'We were looking for fundamental changes and fundamental improvements in technology. Metro *had* to be made as competitively as possible. We had to get the workforce on our side from the start, so to do that we took the senior shop stewards to Turin, to show them the facilities at Fiat. Even though Fiat's Robogate is advanced, it wasn't as completely automatic as the tooling we needed at Longbridge, and we told them that. Then they *began* to understand that working practices would have to change—they'd never seen anything as modern as that, anywhere. We also went to look at Renault, to VW at Wolfsburg, and to Japan, to see what was happening. There was no opposition to this—because these people were showing technology already in use, nothing secret. We'd have to be even better than that'.

All the major body pressings for the Austin Allegro were stamped at the Pressed Steel Fisher factory in Swindon, and sent to Longbridge daily by special train through Stroud and Cheltenham. For the new car, the same system could be applied, but a large new area was still going to be needed where the bodies could be framed, and welded together. No such space was available near to the railway line, on the main site, for most usable land had been built over years ago.

This was where the visionaries, and the works engineers, would have to earn their reputations. Even before Harold Musgrove arrived on the scene, but more especially afterwards, they were encouraged to think big, and to banish the word 'impossible' from their vocabulary. 'Whatever management wants', Harold says, 'we'll give it to them, somehow. Don't ask me how—perhaps I haven't thought about it yet. But we've now got some of the best nut cases in the business working here. They don't only believe, they *know* they're the best in the business!'

But at the beginning of 1977, it looked like an impossible brief. The existing factory had to be kept running, the workforce had to be kept happy, and almost every department had to be reorganised for the 1980s. It could not be done at Longbridge without acquiring new land—and at first sight, there was no more land available.

The genius who made twin breakthroughs is no longer recorded, but his name ought to be recorded, at the very least, by a commemorative plaque. Perhaps the decision to expand the final assembly buildings—by linking one with the other, gutting and re-equipping the interior—was inevitable; buying more land from the local hospital was not.

A look at the map of Longbridge showed that there was a considerable area of open fields behind West Works, to the north west of it. That was the good news—the bad news was that it was owned by, and rather close to, the Hollymoor hospital. Could some land be made available? And, if so, what were the snags?

Fortunately for British Leyland, the enlightened attitude of local authority made the purchase of 33 acres of hospital land possible. Of this, the new building, christened New West Works, covered 17.5 acres, which still left room for further expansion one day, but it was also necessary for a huge earth bank to be thrown up around the buildings, to keep the noise of the building well away from the hospital. In fact, noise levels in New West Works are amazingly low. To level the site, half a million cubic yards of earth had to be moved, and one result is that the Longbridge site now stretches for two miles along the side of the main Birmingham–Bristol railway.

The first of many contracts for the rejuvenation of Longbridge were signed in June 1977, and it was at this point that huge figures—land areas and financial—began to be bandied about. McAlpine got the New West Works job, where the 750,000 square foot building and all its services was priced at £15.5 million, while Wimpey were awarded the £6 million job of rebuilding and extending the Car Assembly Building, adding 250,000 square feet to the existing 350,000 square foot level.

But if the figure were large, the time available was short. 'We had 2½ years to finish the job, ready to start building cars', Harold Musgrove told me. 'It was an exceptionally short time, for most normal lead times in the "Good Old Days" were four to five years. It was almost impossibly short, because we were installing entirely new methods of manufacture as well.'

Things got under way with a flourish in the summer of 1977, but almost came to a halt in the late autumn when ADO88 was ousted in favour of LC8. Perhaps, if ground had not been broken, and tooling had not already begun, LC8 might have been even more different from ADO88 than it actually became. Even as it was, the delay

New West Works at Longbridge, completed in 1980, which now dwarfs 'Old' West Works, behind it in this aerial shot. The main CABs (Car Assembly Buildings) are on top of the hill, to the far top right of the shot.

was considerable, and the tight schedule began to look tighter with every day's delay.

'But don't forget', Harold Musgrove also reminded me, 'that this wasn't the only job we had on. We had the Ital coming at us, at Cowley, and there was a lot of work to do at Drews Lane [where axle parts are made]. I had to treat the Longbridge project as an "evenings and weekends" job for a time. It was nearly impossible to deal with it during the daytime. We had to shut down day-to-day work at about six pm, grab a few sandwiches, then work at the new project until about 11 pm. Sometimes we were in on Saturdays and Sundays, tramping around the muddy site, climbing over scaffolding.'

'Weekends *did* exist—sometimes', said Tony Gilroy, 'though I used to take all my neglected paperwork home then to sort out before Monday. It wasn't much of a life for our families, but I think they all understood we were in a battle for survival . . . .'

A battle for survival? Yes—everyone now seemed to see it as that. In spite of what the hot-heads were saying, and in spite of all the dramas (some real, some trumped up) which got into the newspapers, everyone at British Leyland, from the directors to the teaboys, seemed to have got the message. They weren't operating in a corner, behind closed doors any more. This was the make-or-break project. If they made it, everyone would cheer—if they let the chance slip there probably wouldn't be another chance. Peter Hill's headline in *The Times* of December 21 1979 said it all: 'One last chance for Leyland'. The sub-title told even more: 'Yesterday the Government committed £300 million to BL. Will the money put the company on the road to recovery?'

Making the new buildings was one thing, but equipping them was another thing entirely. For this was no ordinary extension, and no ordinary expansion plan. Apart from its engine and gearbox, the car itself was going to be new from the ground up—and so were the assembly methods. In the 1960s, perhaps even in the early 1970s, the new car would have been built by a huge workforce, often with back-breaking labour methods, mostly by hand. For Metro, everything was going to be different. All the limits of technology were being stretched, and the workers had to be persuaded to look into the 1980s as well.

The process had started even at the styling stage ('We'd been told to plan a car to last through the 1980s', Rex Fleming repeated), and when the rebuilding of Longbridge began, nothing was left to chance. The bill was going to be enormous—a total of investment of £275 million was allocated to the project—but so was the potential. Entirely new levels of productivity were being planned, and in the end Longbridge would be able to produce more cars than ever before.

'The capacity was to be 6,500 Metros a week, using CAB1 *and* CAB2', Harold Musgrove recalls, 'but originally we only planned to have three assembly tracks in CAB1 to give us 4,500 a week. In the end, we were actually getting 4,700 a week *off the first two tracks in CAB1 alone.* Remarkable—my people are like that—it now looks as if we could get 6,500 a week from CAB1's three tracks, and if we throw CAB2 in, once Allegro has stopped, we must be getting close to 8,500 a week capacity.'

(Back in the early 1960s, when Sir Leonard had just seen CAB2 come on stream, and the sensational new Austin-Morris 1100 saloons introduced, he claimed that Longbridge could produce up to 10,500 vehicles a week. But that was when vans and light trucks were still being made in East Works, next to the railway line, and when lots of CKD—Knocked Down—kits were being exported. At best, Longbridge could never build more than 7,500 complete cars before the Metro project got under way.)

For two years, rebuilding operations—throwing up, knocking down, changing around, stripping out—seemed to be going on all over Longbridge. New building work covered three major areas—the vast New West Works (to house body shell assembly), the extensions to the Car Assembly Buildings, and the building of a new Customer Validation Building.

But that was not all. Although it was not planned at first, more than £30 million was spent on the up-dating and modernisation of the A-Series engine and gearbox-in-sump transmission designs. There were new paint shops, new body storage areas, new conveyor facilities, new roller test rigs, water testing facilities, and emission control areas. And that was at Longbridge alone.

At PSF Swindon, a fully automated six-stage press line, over 100 feet long, had to be installed to produce Metro monoside panels at the rate of 480 every hour. This was the largest pressing ever made for a BL car, a one piece shape stretching from the front door hinge pillar to the rear tail lamp corner. That cost £6 millions. At PSF Llanelli, new press lines and paint plant were needed to build front and rear suspension sub-frames. These started as 48 inch steel blanks, but were shaped on automated press lines at the rate of 600 components an hour. That cost £8 million, and the paint facility added £2 million to that. Another £1 million was spent at

Llanelli on plastics component tooling—for items like engine fans, radiator grilles and glove box lids.

The list wasn't endless but sometimes, to hard-pressed buyers, production managers and finance specialists, it must have seemed like it. In many ways it soon turned into a project full of numbers. Before long, at the peak of redevelopment, 190 contractors were involved in the work, and they would eventually expend 30 million man-hours.

If Herbert Austin could have been around to see the work, he would undoubtedly have marvelled at the different scale of things. After all, when he bought the original Longbridge site in 1905, the asking price had been a mere £10,000, and the nominal capital of the original Austin Motor Company Ltd had been £50,000.

At Longbridge in the late 1970s, it was an exciting time, but it was also too harrowing for some. The hours worked were horrendous, and the strain terrific. 'We only managed to cut the time scale to 2½ years by having people working, and working, sometimes it seemed like *all* the time', Harold Musgrove says. 'I won't drive anyone harder than I'll drive myself, they all know that. But at times, behind closed doors, there would be some terrific arguments about things, and no question of me pulling rank either. Some people, though, couldn't take the strain. They were going to topple over. Some did. We had to move them out, find them a quieter place to work. Working on the Metro was only for the toughest . . ..'

It wasn't just the work, the pace, or the terrifying worries about the investment, the car itself, and BL's future. It was the way in which technological borders were being pushed back, the way in which a new factory was being thrown up which was different from anything tackled before—not only at Longbridge, nor at BL, but in British industry as a whole. In 1980, when the work was finished and journalists were allowed in to look at the machinery in operation, the robotics made all the headlines. It is quite true that there were only 28 robot welders in the entire building, but that represented about half of all the Unimate robots in Britain at the time.

A robot welder, incidentally, is not a man-like metal giant which lumbers round lifting, fetching and carrying; it is a sensitive, electronically programmed, spot welding tool which turns, extends, swivels, clamps, spits sparks—and goes on welding panel to panel, hour after hour, quite tirelessly. This, if not typical of everything in New West Works, symbolised what the Metro project was all about. It was one way—not the only way—of bringing the high technology and high productivity into car production, while taking the drudgery, the noise, the heat and the discomfort for manual workers out of it.

But the story of New West Works began much earlier than this, in 1977, when different, more impressive numbers began to occupy the thoughts of the designers. 17.5 acres, 750,000 square feet, covered the whole site, while 4,200 tons of steel work framed the building, and 100,000 feet of electric cable and seven miles of overhead conveyors linked it all together.

Pressings and sub-assemblies had to be brought in by train from Swindon. British Rail, in spite of all the bad media publicity, could guarantee a daily service unless industrial disputes dislocated their service. A spur from the main Bristol–Birmingham line led direct to West Works (it always had, ever since the original building had been erected in the 1910s) and, for the Metro, a new siding put the covered vans, filled with pallets from Swindon, right inside the building, under cover, and in the dry.

From there, panel sets had to go straight into store, and it was this store which caused many headaches. Multi-layered, multi-racked, deep, wide and high, it was more complicated than any Rubic cube, and it needed a computer to handle it. No forklift truck could penetrate—manual access would have increased its size alarmingly. 'Not to put too fine a point on it', Tony Gilroy was able to say after it had been proved satisfactory, 'if the store hadn't worked, the project couldn't have worked. If the pressings didn't come out by computer control, they couldn't be got out by manual methods.'

There had been no choice when designing the store, nor any desire to choose: 'If we'd opted for conventional storage, it would have had to be the size of the whole building! If pressed, we can hold the equivalent of 7½ days' stock of panelling at the rate of 6,500 Metros a week—that's more than ten days' stock at the 1981 rate of 4,500 a week. So we can even put up with a British Rail strike for a short time—but we'd rather not have to try. We don't like the store to be full—that's working capital we'd rather not have standing idle'.

Since the largest major sub-assembly was the under-frame of the car, and it was this component which had already been partly tooled when the change from ADO88 to LC8 took place, the whole framework of New West Works came to pivot round the two 12,500 square foot Kuka machines which could multi-weld up to 72 underframes an hour. The right way, it was decided, to equip the building was to put down the Kukas, then erect the building from the inside out. It sounds Irish, and the Irish ex-Ford specialist Tony Gilroy saw no need to make fun of that fact. To him, it was the only logical way, so the Kukas were laid down, swathed in temporary framing, polythene sheeting, and temporary heater blowers installed, before the steel work of the monstrous factory was even complete.

'I had difficulty visualising where everything was going to fit', Harold Musgrove told me, 'and I didn't have the time to keep traipsing over to look for myself, so I had wooden models made of the plant, so that I could talk to it myself. I was a damned nuisance at weekends when I used to plough through all the mud and kept asking questions about conveyors. People kept saying ''We haven't designed them yet''—we knew where the drop and pick-up points had to be, but we hadn't worked out how to get things from one place to the next. It was all pressure, pressure, pressure—sometimes in appalling conditions.'

The spirit of the people building the premises was remarkable, as was the spirit of those having to keep on building cars while what looked like chaos was all around them. Incidents which look funny now were terrifying at the time they occurred. At Christmas 1979, for instance, with Longbridge already gearing itself up to start building the first Metro body shells, it was discovered that the overhead conveyor spanning the A38 Bristol road, which connected the West Works body complex to the rest of Longbridge, could not accept Metro bodies. For a short time the two heavily capitalised plants were isolated from each other, for there was no other practical way of moving thousand upon thousands of body shells across this busy main road. Longbridge management still recalls the way in which workers turned out over Christmas, in bitter cold, and sometimes in falling snow, to convert the slings and ease the bottlenecks, so that the factory could re-open on time after the holiday break.

To a layman, even to a seasoned motor industry man, the complexities of New West Works were daunting. Electronically controlled multi-welding machines were everywhere, and—when they first began to operate—the eerie lack of overalled workers was obvious. Harold Musgrove was with Ray Horrocks in the building when the first few bodies began to come together. He remembers, quite distinctly, turning to his boss, and quipping: 'Well, this is it. We've either bought the best body plant in the world, or the world's most expensive baler!'

By that time, in fact, Musgrove was fairly confident, for all the major dramas seemed to have been resolved. Now, as he was to repeat so often to journalists in the summer of 1980, it ought to be impossible to build a bad body shell. There had been one time, however, when tooling was still being installed, when it looked as if bodies could not be built at all. The first of the Sciaky automated body framing (ABF) lines—which were 110 metres long, and were the vital points at which underfloor, monosides, roof, and front end met each other for the first time—was put together, and was found not to fit.

Pandemonium. What on earth had gone wrong? Nothing was obviously adrift, and it was not until someone had the wit to inspect the packing cases that clues began to emerge. Somehow, somewhere, on the journey from factory to factory, the case had struck a low bridge. The driver (no names, no pack drill) had never owned up. It was only when contractors tried to match one part to another that a twist was discovered. Rectifying that problem took four months, and the second ABF machine had to be rushed through in its place.

Nor was that all. To check for even greater assurance of accuracy, an LK three-axis machine had been installed in a clinically clean, air-conditioned room, so that the dimensions of completed body shells could be checked at 124 key points. The basis of this measurement was an absolutely flat 30-ton granite block, which had been imported from Canada, on which the complete body shell could stand. There was only one block, but two had to be imported. The first one was smashed as it was being moved into place . . ..

All of which paled into insignificance when the problems facing George Wimpey Ltd in the conversion of CAB1 were becoming obvious. All major work affected CAB1, the assembly building dating back to the early 1950s, when Longbridge was teeming with A30s, A40s and A70s, and when modern thinking was that the components to be built into a car should travel down assembly lines with the cars themselves, rather than being stored *en masse* at the side of the tracks. 'Old CAB1', as it became known, was building Minis of every variety, nothing else, before conversion work began, and squeezed inside were five trim tracks (where body shells were finished), and four final assembly tracks, all rather short, all cramped, and all somewhat antiquated. Shop stewards who had been invited to visit foreign factories during the 1970s knew how far behind the times this building had fallen, but they dreaded the upheaval which was bound to follow the conversion.

The statistics tell only a tiny part of the story—three long trim tracks, and three final assembly lines were to be installed, all 1,100 feet in length—in a CAB1 enlarged by 250,000 square feet. What also had to be considered was that Mini production had to continue—hopefully, undisturbed—while conversion was under way. In 1977, before the first pneumatic drill set up its hammer blows outside the walls, CAB1 was building up to 4,000 Minis a week in two shifts. That rate, it was planned, should be maintained throughout, customers and world markets permitting.

There was nothing magical about the way the job was tackled. 'We started modifying the CAB1 building', Harold Musgrove explained, 'by filling in the big gap between CAB1 and CAB2. First we built one new trim track, moved one old trim operation out of CAB1, started putting in a new final assembly line, and so on, and so on. Once we'd got started, there was a knock-on effect (literally!) which allowed us to

gradually move across the whole building. The crunch came when we needed to take out a whole line, then install a new one—it sounded impossible, for hundreds of tons of gear, and materials, had to be shifted out, then we had to dig a pit, but in all the electric motors, have concrete laid, and build up the new tracks. If we didn't do it THEN, everything would stop, we'd lose production, and men would have to be laid off.

'But we had to have a go. We started stripping things out in advance, preparing as much as we could, on the Tuesday or Wednesday. Then, the theory was, as the workforce walked out for the weekend, our contractors would move in, and work non-stop, for six shifts, to try to get the job done by Monday. We hoped—but at first it looked as if there was no way.

In some places we had to put up tarpaulin screens, to make the place look respectable. But behind the tarpaulins . . . well! Before the change, Sir Michael, and Ray Horrocks, came round to see how we were getting on. It looked really rather tidy—then at the end of the visit, I drew Ray aside, and showed him behind the tarpaulins! He didn't say much. Just looked, then looked at me, looked at the devastation, gently crossed his fingers, looked at me again, and very quietly said: ''Ring me on Monday morning''. But we did it—rather, they did it. It was great. I've never been involved in an operation which went as well as that strip out, and rebuilding job. I rang Ray on Monday, told him the job was done, and—believe me—we were all very relieved, I can tell you!'

The incentive, above all, to get the job done on time was to prove to the world that BL was still in business, still looking to the future; in many ways, Harold Musgrove was quite gleeful about proving all the media Jonahs wrong. The miracle was that the pace of the rebuilding began to take the workforce along with it. Musgrove agrees that one could describe the track workers as 'an excitable bunch', but he also points out, time and again, that they rarely downed tools even when conditions were very sub-standard. 'It didn't matter whether it was snowing, draughty, or the walls had just been knocked down—they kept on building Minis, and that was what we wanted.'

One of the biggest carve-ups of existing buildings was where the bodies were painted, where they were marshalled, and where they were stored before being moved up to the trim assembly tracks. The legacy of piecemeal modernisation, of old practices, seemingly of ages, was that some bodies had been coming across the Bristol road conveyor in bare metal (Body in White—as the industry knows this state), but some were already painted. A new paint shop was needed, more streamlined, more capacious—more efficient.

While rebuilding work was going on, production could best be described as disorganised. With conveyors sometimes out of action, the body shells had to be moved around the site as best they could—which meant 'borrowing' flat bed lorries from departments which really could not spare them, or improvising in other ways. One day, eventually, the job was done, and the new process swung into operation. 'But it didn't last long', Tony Gilroy recalled. 'No sooner had we started sending Metro bodies through the dip tanks than I got a 'phone call from a foreman. ''You're not going to believe this'', he said, ''but we've just lost a body!'' Bodies

Opposite *Checking out dimensions of a completed body shell on the massive stone base of the measuring bay at Longbridge. The first of those stones was smashed while being delivered!*

were going into the electrodip tanks, coming off the slings and disappearing. We had to fish around to get them out, then modify the slings *very* quickly!'

It was that sort of a period, when anything could happen, and anything often did. Gilroy lost count of the number of times whole sections of Longbridge ground to a halt when a contractor's digger or bulldozer cut through a main power cable. If the location of those cables wasn't known at first, it certainly is by now.

The most important new building—the *only* separate new building—'up on the aerodrome', was the Customer Validation Building (CVB for short). At 80,000 square feet, it cost £5 million, and was meant to make sure that Metros going out to the customer were in the best possible condition. Harold Musgrove likes to point to men with mini-vacuum cleaners poking around in the floor of Metros about to leave the building: 'He's the most important man we've got. He gives the customer the right first impression. You don't want to find nuts and bolts on the floor carpets—you'd wonder where they come from, what they *should* be holding down'.

It was all part of the move to retrieve BL's quality image, which had taken hard knocks in earlier years. To a degree, it had to be solved with a degree of overkill. At first it was hoped to put a new water test facility (searching for leaks) in the CVB, but there wasn't space for everything. Water testing was eventually carried out at the end of the re-vamped asssembly lines, and the CVB building looked after any paint and trim rectification which was needed ('cars *do* get damaged on the tracks, sometimes, we'd be fools to deny that'). Finally, three final inspection and valetting lines looked after the fitment of optional extras, the checking out of equipment, and the striping up of individual derivatives. If any paint rectification was to be done, it would have been foolish to add stripes before everything else was complete. Lastly, come the vacuum cleaner brigade, making sure that the Metro was right, not nearly right, before it left for the showrooms.

Perhaps it wasn't a unique facility in Europe at the time, but it probably was the first separate-building facility in the business. It also benefitted existing Minis and Allegros, all of which were re-routed through the CVB, to emerge better, cleaner, and in nicer condition than ever before.

Lastly, the engineers turned their attentions to the engine, and the transmission. It would have been easy—but quite wrong—to leave the design alone, reasoning that what had been good enough for the Mini would be good enough for Metro. But that would not do—for BL's most important new-car project, everything had to be just so. A long and careful look at the tooling revealed not only that it was getting old (the engine, in its original form, had been introduced in 1951 after all), but that better ways of making things had become available. Not only in design changes, but in the modernisation of tooling, of quality control, and of a general upgrading in performance and behaviour, more than £30 million were spent in the machine shops. A became A-Plus, not only to the benefit of the new Metro, but for the improvement of Itals, Minis and Allegros. The A-Plus engine, in fact, made its public debut in the Ital in July 1980.

Five years earlier, perhaps, such a massive, fast-moving, vital project might never have been tackled. Earlier management teams might not have wanted such a revolution, and certainly could not have found the capital to fund it. By the end of the 1970s, not only was management's thinking wonderfully concentrated on survival, and modernisation, but they were able to convince the workforce to co-operate with them. Even when buildings were half-finished, when contractors were swinging

Job done! Another Metro rolls off the final assembly line in CAB1 at Longbridge. All that now remains is inspection, a water test, and a trip through the Customer Validation Building, before the car sets off for its customer.

overhead, running along walkways close to production lines and raising dust in the process, work carried on.

Brian James of the *Daily Mail*, in one of a series of penetrating features about the Metro put it so well: 'Yet the one thing that held a notoriously tough labour force in check was the clear evidence that the cordially-disliked management were working as never before. "I'll give 'em that", says shop stewards' leader Jack Adams, "I've never known bosses get at it like that. Hardly a night when you didn't drive past the plant and see lights burning in the offices . . . or in the sheds where they were tinkering with the car . . .".'

The management team, at this time, came up with a working rule. If possible no one ever slept on a problem, if it could be solved that night. If that meant sending chairman Musgrove's Jaguar down to the local transport café for bacon and egg sandwiches at midnight, that was the way the job was done.

By the end of 1979, however, the emphasis was changing. Red-eyed managers who had to be re-introduced to their children every Sunday afternoon came to see that the bricks and mortar, the computers and the robots, would all be ready in time. Soon it would be time to stop worrying about the buildings, and to start worrying about the cars themselves. Slowly, but surely, production would have to begin. It was a whole new scene. By the beginning of 1980 the project was accelerating rapidly towards its launch date, and thousands of production cars would be needed before then. Was it still possible?

Chapter 7

Launching the Metro
Turning the dream into reality

It was all very puzzling. If the much-vaunted new Metro was to be a 'Car for the 1980s', and if huge new factories were being erected in which to build it, why were the first production-built Metros taking shape in a cramped corner of Old West Works? What feeling, what emotion, had caused this?

It all had to be put down to fear—fear that something could still go wrong, fear that something had been forgotten, and fear that all the Brave New World technology might still not be enough. Harold Musgrove and Tony Gilroy, backed to the hilt by Ray Horrocks, could not wait for the vast new plant to be completed. They had to know.

'Right from the start', Tony Gilroy recalls, 'it became clear to us that we needed to build a number of Metros very early indeed. We needed to prove out the vehicle and the way of building it. It wasn't to be pilot production as you usually know it, for there were going to be far more cars than usual. We knew that if Metro wasn't a success, if it didn't work properly, then BL wouldn't have a future.'

In that corner of West Works, therefore, well away from the hubbub of Mini and Allegro assembly, the first 'off-tools' Metros were made in September 1979, and by the end of October the total was reaching for 250 in all. The shells were put through the normal paint plant, then finally assembled in a quiet part of Longbridge. A few were even assembled in CAB1—not more than 20 in a shift—even before conversion work had been completed. It was all very temporary, but all very necessary. For sure, it cost BL a small fortune, and the facilities were dismantled almost as soon as they had done their job, but no one ever questioned that expense. Put against the £270 million investment being committed to Metro, it was all worth it. No other firm, as far as BL knew, had ever built so many examples of a new model *more than 12 months* in advance of announcement date.

It was not a move born of desperation, nor of impatience, but it was due to the need to know. Experience told the managers that production cars often performed differently from the hand-built prototypes, and that it took time to find out why. They might be heavier, they might be slower, and they might not be as economical. Worse, it might be unexpectedly difficult to put them together, and some suppliers might be making defective components. Too many times, in the past, BMC or British Leyland had put cars on sale before they knew all the answers. Indeed, it was a standing joke in the industry, and among the motoring press, that the first year's customers did the last year's development. But not this time. Not with Metro.

In any case, it was high time that representative cars to the agreed standard were at last to become available, especially for the manufacturing specialists, and the design and development engineers. Even after the change from ADO88 to the more up-market LC8 had been made in January 1978, it was at least a year before a small number of Fully-Engineered LC8 Prototypes could be built. Even this supply—of ten bodies, only seven of which were ever turned into complete cars—was not enough to finish the job. There was a big programme of legislative work to be carried out, not only for our own UK market, but for all the European and Commonwealth territories where the Metro was to be put on sale; some of these cars would have to be totally destroyed in crash tests, or on the body-wracking pavé tracks at MIRA and Gaydon. For Metro, Mark Snowdon's engineers needed more than 40 proving vehicles for this, and other work, the first of which was built in July 1979.

But there were many other departments which needed cars as soon as possible. Representative models needed to be checked out by quality controllers, cost analysts, advertising agents, production managers and even—on loan—major suppliers. Normally, when a major new model of car is being prepared, what are known as 'pilot production' cars (really the first which can be built from fully-tooled components) begin to take shape five to six months ahead of the announcement to the public. Often, due to tooling delays, that time has to be compressed ever further. With Metro, however, it was all going to be very different.

Even though the BL small car project had gradually but inexorably been gathering pace since the end of 1974, there had been a major delay when the crash programme to develop LC8 from ADO88 came about. Although some tooling work was already under way, almost every major outside 'skin' panel had to be substantially altered.

Even in the summer of 1979, with public launch well over a year away, most of the big press tools needed to stamp out these panels had still not been completed. Modern technology, particularly the onset of computerisation, has helped to cut the time needed to transfer the agreed body shape of a full-size styling clay on to drawings, and into instructions to tool-cutting machinery, but the accurate shaping of big and complex shapes still takes a great deal of time and considerable hand work. This, then, was the problem. How could 250—and more—sets of skin panels be produced in a hurry?

'We had to go to extraordinary lengths to get these panels', Tony Gilroy said, 'for although some of the final tools *were* rushed through at Swindon, some panels had to be pressed on 'soft' temporary tooling. So, while the body lines were sometimes not absolutely and clinically perfect, at least they could fit together functionally and correctly.'

The new cars were invaluable. There was never any argument about that. Every department, every team, and every manager who needed to know more about the car could now sample one at first hand. It also enabled the great 'proving' marathons to get under way. In Fred Coultas' design and development departments, drivers could finally get their hands on a representative Metro for a long period. Cars still had to be put through the detailed mill of performance testing, economy testing, wind tunnel checking, and a programme of compliance testing for legislative reasons, but now there were cars which could be flogged around Gaydon, on the motorways, in Europe, and even further afield. 'Getting miles on a car' is essential to any new project, and the Metro was no exception. Many cars were driven all day at Gaydon, away from public gaze, taken back into a workshop for fuel, a quick clean, and perhaps a service. At night they would be out on the public roads, not disguised, but unnoticed by all but the truck drivers, and the insomniacs. 300 miles a shift, up to

3,000 miles a week, was quite normal for a Metro endurance car. Only in that way could the car's true tyre life, brake pad life, in-service record, and component reliability be ascertained for sure. Were the seats still comfortable after eight hours' motoring? What about ventilation? What was wearing out prematurely? Control positions? Headlamps? Wipers? Wind-noise? No computer could predict what would be found.

Meantime, Harold Musgrove and Ray Horrocks had decided to take the workforce into their confidence too. Morale had been suffering throughout the year as news of further losses filtered through—a loss of money by the company, and job losses for some of them—and it was time for them to know what it was all about. By the autumn of 1979, Sir Michael Edwardes' recovery plan was becoming well known— among other things it envisaged the full or partial closure of 13 factories, and the shedding of 25,000 men—and the wage offer for 1980 was only five per cent, plus the start up of a productivity bonus scheme on a plant-by-plant basis. Derek Robinson, the Longbridge convenor, was adamant that this would not be accepted, but the more sanguine workforce were not so sure. In the event, it would take months of debilitating discussion, yet more brinkmanship on both sides, the imposition of the rise over the heads of the negotiating team, and the sacking of Robinson for the crisis to be resolved.

While all this was brewing up, management was holding hour-long meetings to groups of workers, up to 1,000 employees at a time, to explain future new-model plans to them. Not only were they shown the finalised Metro hatchbacks, but they were also given sneak previews of the Morris Ital (the Marina replacement/restyling job), which was due to be launched in the summer of 1980, of full-size styling mock-ups of the revised hatchback Princess front-wheel-drive car (now on the market, as the Austin Ambassador), and even of the existing mock-ups of the LM10 medium sized car, which was still more than three years away from its public. The only car missing was the new 'TriumpHonda'—the Japanese car to be built at Cowley from the summer of 1981—for Honda had not yet sent a prototype of this car over to Britain.

Even so, at this stage it was still not too late to alter the detail design of the Metro, or even the line-up of models to be put on sale. In the spring of 1979, it had been decided to market the car with 12,000 mile (or 12 month) major service intervals, which meant that changes were needed to the capacity of the engine oil filter, to the specification of various suspension pick-up points (which did not require regular maintenance), the water pump/alternator drive belt, the size of the carburettor dashpot, and that a brake pad wear indicator would be needed. In spite of cost pressures which BL wanted to minimise, there was no question of reducing the adanced braking specification, which included two separate hydraulic circuits and complex front calipers.

A styling review held in June 1979 approved of a 20 mm (0.8 inch) increase in the width of the rear track, to improve the looks and the roadholding, and it was also decided to standardise rear mud flaps on all derivatives. The really major addition, however, came in March 1980, when it decided to push ahead with a super-economy version of the car (the HLE model). During development it had become clear that the Metro could be exceptionally economical if set up properly. Now, like Renault, BL decided to combine high overall gearing with a high-compression engine and miserly carburation—the result was quite startling on some cars, and was to lead to one of the most controversial aspects of the entire launch.

There was also still time to make some minor changes to the appearance. The time for altering the shape of major panels, or for changing the engine, transmission, and suspension, was long past, but the decoration—the 'make-up', I suppose one could say—was still not complete. Which was just as well, because some of the directors were not at all happy with the looks of the early cars produced in the autumn of 1979. 'It looked all wrong', Tony Gilroy recalled, 'I was so sick . . . there was this bit of silver round the grille. Fussy, untidy. The indicator repeaters were circular, and mounted up on the side . . . Very messy.' Some of this was unavoidable, due to the way the cars had been built, but there was still time for Rex Fleming's stylists to make final touches to the car. The result, approved and signed off early in 1980, was the car which has now sold in huge numbers.

At the beginning of 1980, too, it was time for the sales, advertising, and public relations to start their campaigns. How was the Metro to be presented to its public? What were the strong points to be advertised? Should they be teased with a lot of early information, or held in suspense until the last moment?

Before the end of 1979, David Boole moved over from Jaguar-Rover-Triumph to BLEO to manage the new Product Affairs division (that's Public Relations to you or I). His first job was not to prepare for the launch of the Metro itself, but to try to correct all the wrong impressions BL saw to be floating around in the media. 'We knew that the Metro would be the most anticipated new model in the history of the British motor industry', David said, 'and we had to be sure that it got off on the right footing.'

The winter before Metro appeared had been an unhappy one for BL. There had been the wage struggle, and the sacking of Derek Robinson, there had been another slide in the market share, and there was far too much speculation about the future. Quite wrongly, BL were being accused of preparing the wrong car at the wrong time—LC10, it was suggested, should have come before the Metro. There was too much chatter about BL preparing 'the last car of the 1970s', rather than the 'First of the 1980s'. 'When I arrived', Boole recalls, 'it was already a matter of being at the stage of "T minus nine months, and counting . . ."'—there was a lot to be done.'

The first phase had already been done. The public, by this time, had been told, time after time, that the Metro would not replace the Mini, but would be built alongside it. To emphasise this, BL had encouraged the motoring press to celebrate the Mini's 20th birthday in August 1979—a formal 21st birthday party couldn't be arranged, for it would clash too closely with the launch of Metro itself. A spate of Mini advertising, at the time, emphasised the Mini's tiny size, its cheeky character, and the way it could squeeze in and out of most traffic situations. Punchlines like 'Nips in and out like Ronald Biggs' (it was the time of the abortive attempt to extradite bank-robber Biggs from Brazil, and from the West Indies), and 'Better in jams than strawberries' were seen all over the country. As a birthday treat, too, BL began selling a limited-production Mini 1100 Special, which not only went faster than usual, but had an extra-luxurious facia and instrument layout, grille, wheels, and those charismatic black plastic wheel arch extensions to remind everyone of the once-famous Mini-Cooper rally cars. The clincher, which finally made it crystal-clear that the Mini was not about to disappear, was the advert which trumpeted this message: 'Like Bostik, it's going to stick around'. Underneath, in a short crisp commentary, came the sentence: 'Nothing will replace the Mini, not even our new hatchback Metro'.

BL's advertising agents, Leo Burnett, first began to discuss their strategy in

January 1980, and before formulating this, they needed to know what motorists were thinking. More than 100 owners of British hatchback cars were interviewed, shown rough sketches of proposed advertisements, even complete cars without badging, theoretically not knowing what it was all about. Among the interesting comments which filtered through were that most of them wanted to buy a British car if a suitable one was made available, and that they nearly all had the impression that British-market Ford Fiestas were mainly built in Spain. Three distinct features of the car were particularly liked—one was the versatile folding capability of the rear seat, one was the exceptional fuel economy possibility, and the third was the promise of not needing to service the car below intervals of 12,000 miles.

It was a start, and a very good start, but BL's public relations staff had to counter the fact that the coming of Metro had already widely been rumoured. By the beginning of 1980, it was big news, even though it was still hiding away behind security wraps, for the project was regularly discussed in Parliament, in the financial pages of the newspapers, and particularly in motoring magazines. Soon—as soon as possible—a coherent launch strategy would have to be developed.

One problem was that as far as Austin-Morris was concerned, it was all going to be rather unfamiliar. Through no real fault of their own making, they had no recent experience to fall back on. The last major new product to come from Austin-Morris had been the Princess of 1975. Even at Jaguar-Rover-Triumph, the sleek and imposing hatchback Rover 3500 saloon had been revealed in 1976, and the controversial TR7 sports car had appeared more than a year before this. For any of them, the last big occasion had been the presentation of the Series III Jaguar XJ saloons in 1979, and this, in truth, had only been the retouching of an already well-known and well-liked car.

Metro, however, was going to be the biggest story anyone at BL had had to handle

One of the cheeky display adverts run by BL in 1979, to emphasise the unbeatable qualities of the Mini.

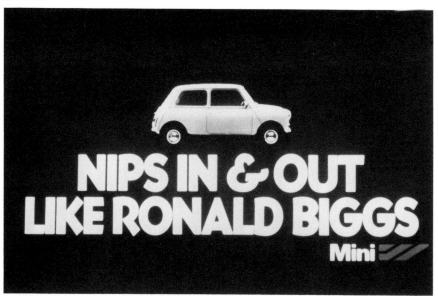

LIKE BOSTIK IT'S GOING TO STICK AROUND.

The Mini is the perfect design for the 80s.

Its small outside so parking's a cinch. Its nippy in traffic so in the Rush Hour it actually rushes.

Its plush inside with all the mod-cons you'd expect. Its very quiet too with comprehensive sound insulation.

And naturally it takes small expensive gallons for long, cheap rides.

So nothing will replace the Mini not even our new hatchback Metro.

Because even in the 80s nothing will move like a Mini.

By 1979, BL wanted the public to realise that the new Metro was not going to replace the existing Mini, as the small print in this display ad (So nothing will replace the Mini, not even our new hatchback Metro . . .) made clear.

in the previous decade, and there could be no question of doing it on a shoestring. Not only the press (and, by definition, the public) but the loyal and long-suffering BL dealers had to be given full details of the Metro, when the time came. But how, and where?

As far as the dealers were concerned, the storm had already broken around their heads. Tony Ball, who was chairman of the British Leyland Europe and Overseas sales and marketing company, was insistent that the dealers should be introduced to the Metro in memorable style, and that their launch should be handled with a great deal of flair. It would have been possible to fly them all off to some exotic continental sun-trap, or herd them all together in a vast conference centre for the complete and show-business 'sight and sound' presentation. But Ball's staff were thinking of doing it all differently—the Metro was to be launched, literally it seemed, at sea!

News about the hiring of the Norwegian-American line's luxury cruise liner, *Vistafjord*, broke in October 1979, when someone in the press noticed this information in Lloyds' list. BL, it seemed, had decided to present the Metro to their dealers on board the *Vistafjord*, in a whole series of parties, on the high seas between Liverpool and the Isle of Man! Naturally, there was something of a furore—mainly, as usual, from those least qualified to comment. How could a state-owned concern like BL, and a loss-making state-owned concern, at that, justify the hiring of a foreign ship, and spending upwards of £1 million on the exercise? And where was the space to drive the car on board a ship?

BL managers were unrepentent. They never needed to deny the rumoured cost of the hire of the ship, and gleefully claimed that they would actually be getting exceptional value for money. One was quoted as saying: 'What is £1 million, when the Metro is costing £275 million to launch? Only 0.36 per cent of the development costs will go on presentation costs. Our main worry is that we are planning to spend too *little* in launching our new car. We must make a splash with Metro. That is why we've decided on the cruise liner.'

But there was still a long way to go before the car could be revealed to the world. Uninformed observers, mostly those with little experience of industry, were still suggesting that the car was going to arrive too late, and that its release should be brought forward. BL were not having any of that. Their target, confidential at first, but soon proudly put on public record, was that more than 6,000 cars would be in dealers' showrooms on launch date in Britain—that every dealer would have cars to be looked at, and cars to be driven.

Tony Ball, chairman and managing director of the sales and marketing division, was adamant about this. Brought back to work for BL in 1978 after 12 years' experience in the retail trade, Ball had originally been a trade apprentice at Longbridge, had become Apprentice of the Year at one stage, and had fronted the successful launch of the original Mini of 1959. Having left BMC, as it then was, in 1967, he had not been involved in a whole series of bodged launches which the pre-Edwardes team had committed, and wanted the arrival of Metro to be a major event, and a major triumph: 'I felt that we were not just looking at the launch of a new car, but that this was the first step towards rebirth of a major company, the re-establishing of the credibility of a *British* motor industry. We had to prove to the world that although we had been down on our knees, we were now capable of bringing BL back from the depths.

'We had to show that Metro was better than the opposition in *every* major respect—in styling, performance, economy (particularly) and in terms of flair. We had to show that Metro had something that no other car could provide. I wanted to bring out an in-born feeling of pride everybody in the country had, that, when our backs are against the wall, we can really fight our way out of trouble.'

One truly major, if not unique, decision taken was that Metro was not going to be kept completely under wraps, but that as much information as possible was to be 'leaked' at an early stage. 'Whatever was supposed to be secret would eventually be discovered by someone, so we had to let information out from time to time and hopefully turn it to our advantage. But we had to walk a tightrope—because we didn't finally want to arrive at announcement day, to find that everybody knew everything about the car, and were sick and tired of the whole process.'

Right from the start, when he took up his post as Ray Horrocks' deputy at Austin-Morris, Tony Ball wanted to involve his dealers as much as possible. The dealer chain had been going through a very difficult time, not only because British Leyland's market share had been falling, but because many smaller dealers had been dropped from the lists. Ball, and his sales force, wanted to reassure those at the sharp end of the selling process, not only that great things were in store for them, but that current models were good, and that quality and reliability was improving all the time.

It was time for a dramatic gesture, and the opportunity presented itself at a major dealer conference at the Wembley Conference Centre, in the autumn of 1978. After being introduced to the dealers, Ball (in his own words) 'had to make the speech of his life', then made the dramatic announcement that dealers were to see what was on the way—the lights on the stage dimmed, and were replaced by flashing disco-style strobes, and suddenly, and very briefly, a Mighty Mini prototype was driven across it. No more, and no less, than that. It was a tantalising glimpse, and it was all the dealers were to be allowed until 1980. But the boost in morale was immediately evident. They knew, perhaps for the very first time, that BL was no longer a talking shop, but a business actually planning for a great future.

One of the nice detail touches of the Metro design was the deep opening hatchback, shown raised in this cutaway drawing.

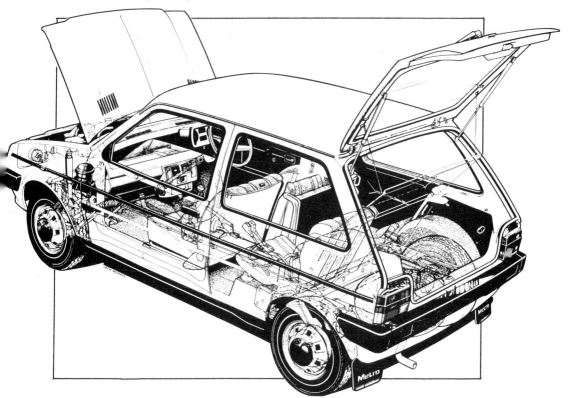

The well-known BMC A-Series Mini/Allegro power pack was completely redeveloped with the Metro in mind, and became the improved A-Plus unit, at a cost of £30 million extra investment.

'But it made the pressure for the launch of the car even more intense. *Of course* the dealers wanted the car launched earlier, but we told them they'd have to wait! So many times in the past, the old company had launched a car, and not had stocks to sell. By the time some people took delivery, the first price increase had had to be made. I was *never* going to have BL in that situation again.'

By the beginning of 1980, David Boole in the Product Affairs department was trying to formulate plans for the press launch of the entire project. At first it was thought that the new car and the new factory facilities should be revealed together, probably by allowing mass drives from London to Longbridge, but in the end it was decided to show off the factory facilities first, in the spring, and to reveal the car later in the summer.

It was already clear that the demand for facilities, and information, was going to be enormous: 'We were absolutely besieged by TV and film companies, well before we could possibly show them anything. ''Teaser'' interviews of Harold Musgrove, leaning on a Metro shrouded in a dust sheet was one thing, but there was no way we were going to let the media into Longbridge at this point. We had to pick and choose. In the end we decided to co-operate with ATV in the Midlands to produce the documentary *A Car is Born*, and BBC's *Nationwide* programme also decided to devote considerable air-time to the project. To help this along, we began to collect footage of the car's development history well in advance.'

No one saw any problem in generating enough interest from the media about the new car, but it was already clear that every move made would be in the full glare of scrutiny, not only from the motoring correspondents, but from the political and financial pundits. Metro, for sure, was already looked upon as a publicly-owned asset, and the public would need to know that their money was being well spent.

This was why there had been such an instant outcry over the choice of *Vistafjord* on which to introduce Metro to the BL dealers. The choice of a press launch location was going to need great care. By this time, too, BL knew that in the autumn of 1980, they would be facing formidable opposition for attention. Not only were Ford proposing to announce a new Escort at the same time as the Metro, but they, too, were turning to the front-wheel-drive philosophy. Ford, of course, although a multi-national concern, was demonstrably successful and profitable—any new model from them was a major event, but the arrival of a front-wheel-drive Escort would be even more important.

'Clearly, it was going to be a major European launch', David Boole told me, 'something which no other company in the British motor industry has to tackle any more. We wanted to launch Metro with great flair, and we wanted to do it in a very *British* style. So that, to us, ruled out a Continental location right away. 'It was going to be the biggest launch we had ever handled, and by the time we'd finished counting, we could see that up to 600 journalists would be involved—about 270 UK journalists, the rest from Europe.'

The only way to do this properly was at a high-class hotel location in Britain, and at one stage four hotels—the Imperial at Torquay, the Gosforth Park in Newcastle, the Gleneagles in Scotland, and the Turnberry, also in Scotland—were on the short list. Somehow, though, none were ideal, for they were all rather remote from London, which is a big problem where foreign journalists are concerned.

However, if the cars were to be revealed to the press in London, and driven by them from their hotel, the question of security had to be considered. In the end, BL decided to ignore all this, for by high summer the public would know a great deal about the cars, and some extra 'sneak previewing' was likely to be good publicity, rather than an embarrassment.

The patriotic, Buy British, Dunkirk spirit, eventually made the choice of only one hotel possible. What could possibly be better than to reveal the Metro at the Churchill, in Portman Square, a hotel carrying the name of Britain's most noted modern statesman? The fact that the Churchill's access to a speedy motorway route out of London was ideal was one thing, and that it was, quite literally, across the square from the company's London headquarters, was another bonus.

Initial plans to show the car to the press in July 1980, and to use no fewer than 60 early-production Metros to do it, were eventually toned down. So many cars, it seemed, could not be available so soon, and Product Affairs finally settled on 30 cars in a variety of specifications, for a launch programme scheduled to take up most of September.

All this, of course, depended on the ability of Longbridge to build the cars—enough of the cars, to the right level of quality—in time. With the launch of the Morris Ital, from Cowley, imminent, and going well, Harold Musgrove was able to turn all his attention to the Metro at last. For the next few months, every member of the workforce at Longbridge would know he was on the site, for his influence was everywhere.

To make the right sort of cars, the tooling had to be made to work correctly, and this took a lot of time in the winter of 1979/1980. Tony Gilroy reminded me that there were no 'slippage days' built in to the timing of the project, so any delays were potentially disastrous. At first, the expensive and vital Unimate welding robots would not sequence properly (this was not at all unexpected, as the electronic controls were formidably complex), and since they were among the first in the country it was necessary to call for help from the United States, where the designs had originated, to get things sorted out. The Kukas and the ABF machines all had their teething troubles, inevitable in a project of this magnitude. It was quickly decided to throw all efforts behind one of the two complete sets of machinery, get that operating correctly, then turn all attention to the second set of machines later. 'We wanted 6,500 cars a week, remember, but even 3,000 a week would do at first.'

Even when the condition of the first body shells was considered satisfactory (and that took time, for Harold Musgrove's idea of an unblemished skin panel was very demanding indeed), there was often a lot wrong with the bought-in components to be fitted to them. The first of the Metro production lines was slowly brought into use and, at first, it was literally building 10 cars a week—not 10 a shift, but 10 a week.

'I wasn't satisfied with the quality of some components going into the first cars', Harold Musgrove remembers. 'If ever I walked down the side of the tracks, there would be a crowd of operators ready to grab me. One once said: "That * * * * car has been past me four times, and I've changed it four times. When are you going to make up your mind, what *do* you want?" So I said to the crowd, "OK, anyone here who can show me a change that hasn't been made for the better, speak up now". There wasn't a sound. "Right then", I said, "shut up, and try again!" At times like that, perhaps it helped if I put on a bit more Brummie accent, and if they were going to shout at me, I was going to shout back.'

Perhaps he would never claim the honour for himself, but there wasn't any doubt that Harold Musgrove was the man of the hour. He was forthright, assertive, cocky even, but he always seemed to know what standards were required. The workforce knew it, and recognised it. Best of all was the fact that the gaunt-faced managing director spoke their language—urgently, accurately, and at length. They knew that he was with them—he was one of them.

Even so, it all took a lot of getting used to, especially for the workers in the technologically advanced areas of the factory. In the good old days, ever since moving tracks had been installed, it had needed an electrician, a union member, to press the button to start the tracks rolling at the beginning of a shift. Now, with the 1980s looming up, even this happened automatically. In the very beginning, the workers couldn't quite bring themselves to believe it. As 8 am approached, clusters of men used to stand around consulting their watches—and at 8 am, when an electronic signal saw the tracks spring into life, there was a perceptible start. This was the Brave New World. Could it work like this all the time?

Harold Musgrove and Tony Gilroy, his manufacturing director, thought that it could, but they still needed to know that the right sort of Metros were being built. Among Musgrove's fighting words to the journalists who visited Longbridge in

Above *Robot welding guns, computer controlled, working on a new Metro body shell at Longbridge.* Below *New Metro shells drop into one of the two ABF (Automated Body Framing) lines where computer-controlled welding guns take over the job humans used to do.* Overleaf *Not a human being in sight but fast-moving robot arms, on each side of part-completed Metro shells at Longbridge, get on with their job in any case.*

One of the incredibly complex but versatile Unimate 'robot' welding guns, which perform so many jobs at Longbridge in the new Metro factory.

April 1980, to see the automatic machinery at last in action, was the claim that: 'I think you will agree, when you have seen these facilities, that it will be *impossible* to build a bad car'.

At this time, and in the privacy of his office, he was not yet convinced. Although production was slowly due to build up for five months before the Metro was made public, he and his staff were still finding problems with the early cars. A personal letter went out to every supplier which effectively said, 'You make a mistake on Metro, and we drop you at once . . .'. That was a lot of letters, to a lot of suppliers—more than 400 of them, even at the start.

The first cars to be built entirely 'off-tools', which in motor industry language means that all the series-production components were being used, were not sent out into a delivery compound, but were immediately taken out on the roads of the West Midlands by the management team. 'We worked in the factory all day, then went out driving for much of the night, looking for rattles, squeaks, knocks and bumps. We wanted to know what didn't fit, and what was going to break.'

It was a worrying time for, by their new high standards, there were problems—many problems. Many of the cars were stripped out completely to search for improvements. Many cars, built on the new production facilities, were never sold off to the trade. The workforce could sense that this was no ordinary new car, and no ordinary management attitude; they offered their own opinions, found their own

Sir Michael Edwardes, BL's dynamic chairman from November 1977, whose first major success was to see the Metro finally into production by the summer of 1980.

problems, and suggested ways of rectifying them. It was heartening, and morale crept up steadily.

By the beginning of August, however, with the single assembly track still moving very slowly, in fits and starts, the crunch point had arrived. 'At this stage', Musgrove recently stated, 'Tony Gilroy was having hysterics at me, for I was still sending batches of cars back. He was asking me for a promise that I wouldn't change anything after the holiday lay-off, but I still wouldn't give him that choice, because we weren't yet satisfied. Finally, one night, Mark Snowdon, Ray Bates, myself and a few others took six new cars out round Warwickshire in the middle of the night, *and* the Metro's main competitors, which we'd had for some time. We kept stopping, talking, switching from car to car, checking and rechecking—but by about four o'clock in the morning, I was satisfied.

'I went home to bed for a few hours, and got back in to my office at about eight o'clock, but not some of the others—Oh no! They'd been at work all day, the day before, driving most of the night, then working through to get the car's completely modified for the morning, and *then* they kept on through the day. I've never seen anything like it. But this time we were all happy. We got one car completely up to the agreed standard, in every little detail, then I rang Ray Horrocks. "Ray, that's it now", I said, "give it a try." He drove the car, agreed with us, and left me to it. Ray's like that.'

From that moment, in the third week of August, Austin-Morris were over the hump. They were past the post, and there was no holding back now. May to July had truly been for pilot production, for climbing the learning curve. Tony Gilroy finally got the signal, and Metros start to flood out of New West Works, across the conveyor into the new paint plant, hanging securely on the slings which had repeatedly dropped them only months earlier, and finally began to inch their way, station by station, down the first of the 1,100 foot long assembly tracks in the rejuvenated CAB1 building. The rate simply rocketed up from the end of August. 'After that', one manager told me, 'it was just like shelling peas.'

The public relations machine had already begun to swing into action. Controlled leaks to responsible newspapers, to magazines, and to the rest of the media, had proliferated during the spring of the year so it was no surprise when, in May 1980, *Car* magazine published one of their well-known 'Scoop' columns. This time their facts were almost entirely accurate, and their opinions largely complimentary.

By and large, the press had been much impressed by their first view of the space-age Longbridge production equipment. Only tantalising glimpses of Metro body shells had been available in New West Works (not even the most dedicated embargo-breaker could make much of an unpainted pressed-steel floor pan) but it was enough to fire up the imagination of the headline writers: 'BL Lifesaver is ready for the road'; 'The Metro Miracle Workers'; 'Getting it right—on Metro Line'; 'An Automatic success!'—and, from the *Morning Star*: 'Star Trek?—No, just BL'. One writer, searching for a new angle, even found time to say: 'Even the Air is just right', having picked up the fact that the seven New West Works computers were housed in their own air-conditioned complex.

A few weeks later, Ken Gooding of the *Financial Times* made a reasoned and quite dispassionate survey of the new car's prospects, which included these comments: 'The introduction of highly-automated production systems for body building and assembly at Longbridge will put BL on an equal footing with its international rivals. Output at Longbridge is planned to improve from the current 16 to 17 cars a year per man employed, to 20 this year, and 30 by the end of 1981. At that stage it would be up to the best Japanese standards. BL plans to build steadily from an initial 3,000 a week to 6,500 by the second quarter of 1981 . . .'.

These high hopes were based on the fact that the 'Gross Line Efficiency' (the amount of time that the production lines were actually building cars) was due to be drastically improved. 'We'd been manning for up to 3,500 Minis a week, but were regularly only achieving 2,300, which was pretty awful', Harold Musgrove said. 'It was sheer bloody incompetence on our part. For the Metro we were talking of GLEs of more than 95 per cent.'

The press car garage, which had been tearing its hair out at the delay in getting hold of production-standard Metros, finally began to turn out complete cars. A whole series of registration numbers, starting at GJW301W, were taken out on August 1, and the frantic build up to advertising the publicity campaigns could begin. But where, what, and how to advertise? Tony Ball, whose enthusiasm for the Metro had been growing for nearly two years, decided that the presentation of the new car should lean heavily on the theme of patriotism. Leo Burnett, the agents, came up with the very effective sub-heading: 'A British car to beat the World', and their treatment of TV commercials was a complete parody of the Churchillian spirit.

Their theme in this spot was that the Metros were out to repel the foreign invaders. Accordingly, a fleet of Metros were to be seen rushing through picturesque

British villages on the way to the South Coast, where they would line up, threateningly, in a phalanx, on one of the famous 'white cliffs', glowering down on a landing craft which was attempting to disgorge Renaults, VWs and Fiats, to take over our roads.

With 14 Metros involved, and with all the panoply of cameramen, sound recordists and scene decorators on hand, it wasn't a session that could be kept secret. The villages used were Lavenham and Kersey, in deepest Suffolk, while the most appropriate 'white cliff' that could be found was Handfast Point in Dorset, only a few miles from the busy holiday resort of Bournemouth.

The *East Anglian Daily Times*, and the *Evening Star*, both local Suffolk newspapers, were not likely to miss a newsworthy scoop like that, and both subsequently carried major features about the work. On Tuesday, August 5, the *Evening Star*'s front page headline was 'Wraps Off!', sub-headed 'Oops! It's the Mini Metro', with the added comment that 'The *Star* brings you the pictures tonight you shouldn't see until October'. *The Daily Times* contented itself with the more sober: 'Leyland's hush-hush car gets maximum exposure in rural setting'.

Scurrilous rumours spreading among the press at the time suggested that at least one Metro—that placed at the very tip of the vee-shaped cliff—had actually fallen over the edge at one point in proceedings, but Tony Ball denies it with a great hoot of laughter: 'It's a good story, but it isn't true. What did happen was that Dave Allen, the Irish comedian, asked if he could re-stage part of the commercial, so that one could appear to be falling off, but we wouldn't agree. That sort of publicity we could do without!'

In the meantime, Britain's most respected motoring magazine, *Autocar*, had developed the bright idea of not only driving the car ahead of launch date (which would have been granted to them, in any case), but of subjecting it to the sort of endurance test which could prove or disprove its worth. Editor Ray Hutton accordingly persuaded the BL public relations staff to lend him a car, so that they could attempt a '5,000 miles in five days' driving stunt, which would start and finish from London's Westminster Bridge, and would take in flying visits to Paris, Lisbon, Madrid, Rome, Zurich, Vienna, Frankfurt, Amsterdam and Brussels. To get the best of both worlds, it was decided that the 1.0-litre engine should be used, in a car having the HLS trim—not a car which would actually be put on sale in that form, but one which would still be very representative of the type. Fred Coultas' engineers at Longbridge prepared the car—one of the very first 'off-tools' models—in which the only important non-standard item was the extra, second, Mini fuel tank in the left side of the luggage boot area, and in which an early example of the optional Smiths trip computer was fitted to the facia panel. All in all 14 drivers were involved—one of which was *Autocar*'s lady road tester, Margaret Wentworth, and one was myself.

5,000 miles in five days! It doesn't sound impossible—nor was it—but it was still a formidable undertaking. Ray Hutton himself drove the car away from Westminster Bridge at midnight on Sunday/Monday, August 31/September 1, and it was due back there, in my hands, before midnight on Friday, September 5. If we had worried beforehand, the trip itself was almost entirely routine, and free from incident. Lisbon was visited on Tuesday at 1.30 pm, Rome on Wednesday near midnight, and Vienna on Thursday at 11.00 pm. A BL back-up team insisted on changing a 'tappy' tappet at Frankfurt airport on Friday morning before I left on my 624 miles stint with a photographer, but we still managed to visit Amsterdam and Brussels, take photographs as 'proof of passage', *and* catch the 5.45 pm cross-channel ferry from

Above *Midnight, Sunday/Monday August 31/September 1 1980, and* Autocar*'s 5,000-miles-in-five days car prepares to start from London's Westminster Bridge. Editor Ray Hutton is driving, and BL's Peter Harris sets the trip computer.* **Above right** *Half-way round, technical editor Michael Scarlett poses the car in Pisa.* **Right** *Less than five days later the gallant little 1.0-litre Metro was back on Westminster Bridge again. Wielding the champagne is photographer Peter Cramer, with the author sheltering behind the car, out of range of spraying bubbly.*

Calais, before arriving cheerfully back opposite Big Ben at 9.30 pm on the Friday. After the traditional champagne-spraying ceremony, we all repaired to Ray Hutton's flat where a monumental party developed. It was generally agreed that, while none of the drivers were particularly keen on the idea of losing a night's sleep to drive round Europe again just yet, the Metro itself was quite capable of doing another circuit!

As a postscript, *Autocar* retained the car for several more weeks, and eventually put it on display on their stand at the NEC Motor Show in October. Their great rivals, *Motor*, were furious. Incidentally, the down-beat end to this great endeavour was that while the Metro was resting on the stand, one of its rear tyres gradually and quite unstoppably deflated . . . .

After groups of distinguished politicians, public figures, industrialists, trades union leaders, and opinion formers in general, had all been invited up to Longbridge to see the car, and the new facilities, it was time to begin the formal launch of the car to journalists. Starting from August Bank Holiday Monday, groups would arrive at the Churchill Hotel, in Portman Square, at the end of one day, where they would immediately be presented with a tightly-packed timetable listing the displays, the presentation, the discussion groups, and the driving opportunities they were to have in the next 24 hours. It was no booze-and-cabaret trip (that sort of occasion tends to

exist in fiction, and in TV series, rather than in fact), but each journalist nevertheless was given a blue sweater, British made, with the word 'Metro' delicately picked out in a symbol on the left breast. It was that sort of occasion—downbeat, proud and infinitely patriotic.

The morning's driving session followed a fast route out into the Cotswolds, a coffee stop at a beautiful castle near Banbury, a return to the Henley-on-Thames area, and dispersal after lunch. No junketing, nothing taken to excess, and an excellent opportunity to learn all about the Metro's behaviour. The public, especially motorists going the same way, were agog. This procession, repeated on 20 days, attracted a lot of attention, and innumerable journalists told tales of making phenomenal avoidances to miss gawpers, or transfixed day-dreamers, while several of us were stopped on the M40 (London–Oxford) motorway by sinister-looking policemen who only wanted to get a better look at the new model. The cars themselves had black taping over their badges, but nobody was fooled. Everyone, it seemed, knew that this was the new Metro; everyone, it seemed, approved.

By this time it was asking too much for no sneak preview pictures to be taken of the car. 'The journalists themselves were asked to respect an embargo of October 8 1980', David Boole says, 'but we couldn't expect those not involved in the launch to stick to this. But there was one occasion when the Associated Press picture agency sent a photographer out to snap cars as they were leaving the hotel one morning—we were fair game, by then—and that picture went round the world.'

This apart, there were no disasters, and no accidents. Only one of the cars, it seems, was even scraped. There was one occurrence, however, which BL never mentioned at the time, because it was really rather embarrassing. Over one weekend, when the cars were parked in a multi-storey car park not far from Portman Square, one of them disappeared!

David Boole can now joke about this, as it all ended happily: 'We lost one car, literally lost it. One was stolen, over a weekend, and it didn't turn up until a few days later, parked among a line of ordinary cars in a street in South London. There it was, a bright yellow Metro 1.0L, parked out in the street, and no newspaper or TV station ever found out about it'. How did it happen? 'We're still not sure, though there was no question of the car having been burgled. Someone had found a set of keys, had worked out which car they fitted, and had simply driven off in it, joy-riding. But it was found, undamaged, and quite complete. Amazing!'

At the same time, the much-publicised series of *Vistafjord* cruises had been taking place, to introduce the dealers to the car which they would soon be able to start selling. Once again, it was a down-beat occasion, probably being carried out at less cost than if massive hotels and conference facilities had been hired in Britain itself. ('It really *was* cheaper to do it this way—I suppose if we'd been cruising up and down the Caribbean, there might have been some cause for complaint', said Tony Ball). Dealers boarded *Vistafjord* in Liverpool, enjoyed a two-way cruise, to and from the Isle of Man. A fleet of Metros was on the island, ready to be driven around the roads which, in early September, were almost denuded of tourist traffic. The only minor miscalculation BL made here was that rally crews were already in the Isle of Man, practising for the forthcoming International event, and the two groups sometimes found themselves on the same roads; the Manx territory, after all, is tightly constructed.

Tony Ball is adamant that the choice of the cruise ship *Vistafjord* was right, had flair, and meant that every BL dealer was happy to attend. 'We needed a captive audience, we needed lecture facilities, and adequate hotel facilities. *Vistafjord* had all these, and of course the Isle of Man roads were ideal, well out of the way of most prying eyes.'

There were occasions when the seas were so rough that *Vistafjord* had difficulty in docking at Douglas harbour, and once it had to slip round to the other side of the land mass to find sheltered quays. On the day in which BL Cars' chairman, Ray Horrocks, had to leave *Vistafjord* to attend a major meeting in London with Sir Michael Edwardes, the ship could not make a landfall at all. The hapless Ray Horrocks had to be taken off the luxury ship by lifeboat, and lowered into it by breeches-buoy, with a gleeful Tony Ball in charge!

The dealers, at last, were on the verge of getting a very charismatic new model to sell, and nearly all of them seemed to react well to BL's very patriotic presentation. I can certainly believe that the car was finally unveiled to them to the choral strains of Elgar's Pomp and Circumstance march, *Land of Hope and Glory*, but can it really be true that grown men, businessmen with a lifetime of experience, wept at the sight of it all? Apparently they could, and did.

Even before the car was ready for sale, however, it was making controversial head-lines. An early example had been loaned to the Automobile Association for their assessment, where testers had put it through a well-established performance and economy routine. BL had prepared a completely standard Metro 1.0 litre car—their super-economy HLE derivative—and were expecting to hear good results from such an unbiased source. It was during the Churchill Hotel journalists' sessions, however, when the AA's astonishing discovery was revealed—that their Metro, undoctored in any way, had been tested for fuel consumption, and had notched up no less than 83 mpg at a steady 30 mph.

This was a remarkable figure, even if it had been achieved in very special conditions. No motorist was likely to drive his car around at a steady 30 mph in top gear for very long, so in that respect it was a rather artificial test, but it did point out the overall efficiency of the latest A-Plus engine. 83 mpg was so high that no journalist could remember ever having seen it achieved anywhere else. BL, for their part, were delighted, but a little wary of the implications. It was the sort of story that the newspaper headline writers would fasten on, and it would be all too easy for some motorists to expect their new Metros to be as economical all the time!

By the end of the summer, preparations for launching the Metro were almost complete, but it was one of those wonderful projects where some new opportunity for publicising its arrival was always arising. Even though the technology of the Metro was brand new, and forward-looking, it also just happened to be coming along in 1980, which was the 75th anniversary of the birth of the Austin Motor Company, and of the foundation of Longbridge as a car-making plant.

BL had also been granted the accolade of a royal visit to Longbridge, for HRH Prince Charles, the Prince of Wales, had agreed not only to make the trip to inspect the new car, and the new facilities, but to perform the official opening of the extensions. Since Prince Charles is known to be a keen driver, there was not going to be a problem in persuading him to try a Metro—the problem might be in tactfully getting him out of it again.

By September, nothing could now stop the arrival of Metro, and nothing was likely to deaden its impact on the world. The influential motoring magazines had already completed their detailed technical analyses, and their informative cutaway drawings. The 'long-lead' colour magazines, who needed material two months ahead of

Above *HRH Prince Charles, the Prince of Wales, with Harold Musgrove (right), on a tour of BL's Metro facility at Longbridge while carrying out the official opening of the New West Works in October 1980, and* **(below)** *studying a finished but unpainted Metro body shell.*

publication date, had been, and gone. The 'new' Longbridge, as an ultra-modern car-manufacturing plant, was up and running. All Tony Gilroy's hard work had paid off, and all Harold Musgrove's face-to-face exhortation of his total workforce was at an end. With at least one of all the duplicated assembly lines in operation all over Longbridge, more and more Metros were being slotted together in the way it had always been planned. Before announcement day, more than 6,000 cars had to be with BL dealers all over Britain. In August, that figure had looked impossible, and in early September, it still looked doubtful. Before the end of the month, however, the atmosphere at Longbridge became tangibly less tense. Everything was going well. It *was* going to be all right on the night.

D-day was Wednesday, October 8 1980. BL management held its breath. They had to wait for the verdict of the media. Then, and only then, it was up to the customer.

Chapter 8

Metro makes its mark
The first year

Anyone in Britain who didn't realise that BL were announcing the Mini Metro on Wednesday, October 8 1980, must have been out of the country. BL didn't need to make their own big effort, for the media did it for them; it was the Main Event of the day. It was almost as if the Battle of Britain had been won all over again. There were headlines in the national newspapers, lead stories on radio news programmes and lengthy coverage on television. Features analysing the car, the people involved and the project began to appear all over Britain. The motoring magazines, of course, had a field day.

It was almost all good news. No one, it seemed, had a bad word to say about the car, or the bravery of the company in committing so much money to a single project. The delight in Portman Square, and at Longbridge, was nearly tangible. You could almost hear the sighs of relief. It was going to be OK after all. The first hurdle had been cleared. The media had been friendly and the Metro had got off to a flying start.

In many ways, it was something of a miracle, for there was nothing unexpected about the car's arrival when it came. The project, after all, had been rumoured since 1975, discussed in some detail since 1978, given its name in 1979 and analysed from every possible angle throughout 1980. Yet the public had never seemed to tire of it all. Even after all this time, the interest shown in the Metro, when it finally made its bow, was enormous.

There had been nothing like it, in the motoring world, since Ford had launched their original Capri sports coupé in 1969. On that occasion, Capris were parked outside most important railway stations on the morning of the launch. On that occasion, too, Ford did not begin delivering cars until some time later, and thus got two separate bursts of publicity for their new model. BL, without even remembering what had been done by their rivals in the past, settled on much the same strategy.

Although the Metro was revealed to the world on October 8, it did not actually appear in the showrooms, or go on sale, until the following week, on October 14, a date carefully chosen to precede opening day of the British Motor Show, at the National Exhibition Centre, near Birmingham. This was a deliberate piece of strategy. BL did not want to put their vitally important new car on sale on the opening day of the show, when it might be swamped by other announcements, and they also wanted to give *all* their customers the chance to have their own, personal, motor show, in the local showrooms. Neither did it escape their attention that to do this might divert attention from rival offerings which were just being put on show at the NEC!

Accordingly, there was no Metro advertising in the first week, for all the coverage provided by the media made it quite unnecessary. The *Birmingham Evening Mail*—the Metro's 'local' newspaper—produced an extremely well-researched supplement inside one of its issues, *The Times* had a major feature headlined 'Can the Metro save BL?', and the *Daily Express* ran an interview by David Benson, with the Metro's technical supremo, Mark Snowdon. The *Daily Mail* went even better, by running centre-spread stories over three days, starting on the Monday before launch, and ending on launch day itself. These features, written by Brian James, were penetrating and very well informed, but were graced with headlines such as: 'The men who gave all for a mistress called Metro!'. There was more—much more—like this.

Engineering enthusiasts, who wanted to know every detail of the car's technical layout, avidly bought the two major British motoring magazines—*Autocar* and *Motor*—to read the design and development stories. Both surveys were very detailed, and both were enthusiastic about the car, as revealed to them. *Autocar*'s coverage—a nine-page technical story, and an 11-page story about the 5,000-miles-in-five-days Metro drive, briefly mentioned in the last chapter—was as much as any potential customer needed to know about the car. *Motor*'s coverage was more conventional, but it included a styling story by Brian Hatton, and a penetrating analysis of the ADO74/ADO88/LC8 development story by Philip Turner, in an interview with Mark Snowdon.

However, even the specialist magazines could not treat the Metro as 'merely a motor car'. *Autocar*'s opening words summed things up beautifully: 'One can't talk about the Metro without talking politics. Never has the development of a new model been so fiercely subject to public gaze. Confidentiality, in the way that the motor industry understands it, has never really existed for BL's new baby. Even before it was conceived, every kind of meddler, from the informed to the ignorant, from spurned industrialists to revolutionary union leaders and publicity-seeking Members of Parliament, had their say about the car, the cost of the project, and how and where it should be made. Metro had every possibility therefore of being a ''committee car'' of the worst kind. That it had not turned out to be so is a tribute to BL's current management . . .'.

The first thing to be made clear by the motoring press was not only that BL were introducing a new six-model Metro range, but that they were reducing and re-shaping the Mini range to make way for it. Until the Metro arrived, there had been nine Minis in three shapes—'original', long-nosed Clubman, and long-wheelbase Clubman estate—and four different engine sizes, ranging from 848 cc to 1,275 cc. Clearly the Metro was going to clash with the more up-market Minis (and could be expected to kill them off very quickly indeed), so BL decided to pre-empt this right away.

As soon as the Metro was announced, therefore, BL reduced the Mini range to just three cars, all with the 998 cc engine, called Mini City, Mini HL, and Mini HL Estate. To make way for the Metro, both on the production lines at Longbridge, and in the market place, all the Clubman derivatives, including the 1275GT, were dropped.

Technically, the motoring press made much of the way the concept had evolved through ADO88 to LC8, and of the advanced technology being employed in manufacture. There was high praise for the impressive torsional stiffness of the body shell (5,800 lb ft/degree, compared with 4,650 lb ft/degree for the Fiesta), for the high degree of barrier crash protection conferred by features like the steering column which was only pushed back towards the driver by fractions of an inch, and the interlocking door/door sill joints, for the neatly detailed grille (and its aerodynamic capabilities), and for the excellent aerodynamic qualities of the car as a whole.

Neither had it escaped the analysts that BL were not proposing to offer two established safety features (Triplex 10/20 windscreen glass and 'run-flat' Dunlop Denovo tyres) on which much previous emphasis had been laid. BL expressed great sorrow that other manufacturers had not followed their example, and that the unit costs of such items was still distressingly high. In any case, there had always been consumer resistance to the purchase of Denovo tyres, for it had always been difficult to convince them that they should spend more money on fewer tyres (no spare wheel was fitted when Denovos were specified), or that Denovo service would always be available when they needed repairs, even at weekends and holiday periods.

Much, too, was made of the truly practical features of the new design—not only the hatchback, but the asymmetric folding of the rear seat, the 12,000 mile service intervals, and details such as the brake pad wear warning lights.

When Fiat had introduced their utilitarian Panda, earlier in the year, they had pointed out the space being offered, and used an American-inspired standard of 'passenger space efficiency' to prove their point. This compared a car's overall length with the sum of the maximum front leg room and the 'couple' distance between front and rear passengers' hip joints. It was a mistake. Fiat's Panda might have been good, but other cars were better.

The Metro was best of all. Its PSE ratio was 50 per cent, a full percentage point better than its great British rival, the Ford Fiesta, and nearly three percentage points better than continental competition like the Fiat 127, the Renault 5 and the VW Polo. It didn't really matter if the public—even the technical public—were unsure about the origins of the PSE factor; the figures proved that the Metro was the most roomy of all.

It was also a complete range of cars, right from the start, with several other derivatives known to be under consideration. From 44 bhp to 63 bhp, and (in Britain) from £3,095 to £4,396, there were six derivatives:

Metro	The 'base' model, 998 cc and 44 bhp.
Metro	The 'fleet' option, 998 cc, 2-star fuel, 41 bhp.
Metro L	Higher trim and equipment spec, 998 cc, 44 bhp.
Metro HLE	The super-economy version, high-compression 998 cc, high gearing, 46 bhp.
Metro 1.3S	High-spec, 1,275 cc, 63 bhp, HLE gearing.
Metro 1.3HLS	Luxury-spec, with 1.3S mechanicals and gearing.

At the start there was no automatic transmission option, but this was known to be under way.

BL's competitors, by all accounts, tried very hard to find shortcomings in the Metro, so that they could re-advertise their own products with advantage—but found it very difficult. In most respects, the charts published in the motoring press showed what a good, well-thought-out, car the Metro really was. In particular, Metro proved to be a very roomy car, with an outstandingly large 'gross cargo' figure of 45.7 cubic feet, and was the widest car of all across the occupants' shoulders. Even so, it was the shortest car of all in its class, and only marginally wider than the Renault 5 and the Fiat 127. Its aerodynamic drag coefficient was the lowest of all, and as a consequence its 'official' Department of Transport fuel consumption figures were quite outstanding.

Even before the NEC Motor Show opened, Tony Ball was exuberant about Metro's prospects, and once he had seen the reaction of the press he was quite euphoric. All the pre-launch work had been worthwhile, public response had been favourable—now the aggressive advertising, and marketing, could begin.

'Metro was the key to the recovery of BL', Tony Ball said some months later, when reviewing the car's progress, 'so we had to take up a strongly patriotic stance. That's why our advertising all used the theme of "A British car to beat the World". Incidentally, although we used the "Mini" name in the title, as displayed on the actual hatchback of the cars, this was to emphasise the link between the Mini and the Metro (as if anyone hadn't already noticed). In the end we felt that the public would soon merely come to call the car the Metro—which they now have—but we wanted to bridge the gap between Mini and Metro by launching the car like that.' In the display advertising, however, the car was always very simply placarded as 'Metro'.

If any other concern had gone in for advertising of the type seen around Metro, they might have been accused of going 'over the top', but somehow, with the Metro, the public seemed ready to look fondly on such excesses. Leo Burnett, the advertising agents, had gone right along with Tony Ball's edict to stress patriotism, and their copywriters had spent weeks wallowing in Britain's history to get the flavour of the occasion. The object, it seemed, had been to look for famous Englishmen, or their

Below *'A British car to beat the World'—the advertising message is clear in this spacious stand display at the 1980 Motor Show.* **Overleaf** *The Metro advertising was striking, patriotic, even chauvinistic, to say the least. The copywriters at Leo Burnett had had a field day.*

45·7
CU.FT

METRO

METRO

METRO

EVEN WELLINGTON
NEVER IMAGINED
A BOOT THIS BIG.

ordinary hatchback, the back seat or down. In a Metro, it does both at e time.

because the asymmetric Split-Action divided one third/two thirds, it's y versatile.*

the smaller seat down and two can sit comfortably beside a neatly carry cot or trunk. Fold the wider side nd you can carry a mountain of luggage ne back seat passenger.

both seats down and the amount of rrying space is truly enormous: 45.7 et.

at beats the Renault 5, lo, Fiat 127 and esta.

AT SPACE FOR GREAT BRITAIN.

e new Metro is so roomy and com- e CAR Magazine (May 1980) said)…stands to be the most space- t volume car in history."

e newly designed seats are contoured e long drives feel miles shorter. While glass area means greater visibility, and e spacious 'feel' all round.

e doors are extra wide and the front don't just fold forward; they slide rd and automatically return to exactly they started.

e back seat has enough room for three -ups to sit in without wishing they grown up.

omfort is increased by specially de- d Hydragas℠ suspension. And quietness ilt into the design at the beginning he help of a structural vibrational is in an anechoic (echo-free) chamber.

1PG, NEVER BEFORE HAVE SO Y GONE SO FAR ON SO LITTLE.

Vith its new A-Plus engine and refined, ve gear box Metro delivers great per- nce and great economy.

he 1.3S and HLS top 96MPH and zip 0-60MPH in 12.3 seconds.

Vhile the HLE, at an independent test rmed by AA engineers, achieved a rkable 62MPG at a steady 50MPH. hat's not all. At a steady 30MPH the got an astounding 83MPG.

WITH 12,000 MILES BETWEEN SERVICES, METRO RULES THE BAYS.

Metros go 12,000 miles or one full year without a service. (The Fiesta, Polo, Datsun Cherry, Renault 5 and Fiat 127 all recommend services every 5000 or 6000 miles.)

Every Metro has brake pad wear sensors to tell you when to change the brake pads.

Self-cleaning sliding contact points are standard, as is a long-life battery which only needs topping up once a year.

Features like these, backed by the com-puterised precision of the new automated West Works at Longbridge, means Metros will stay on the road while other cars are in the garage.

SAFE AS THE CROWN JEWELS.

Metros have safety designed in from the start.

A reinforced steel passenger compart-ment has impact-absorbing front and rear zones. And the floor sills are designed to interlock with the doors to give extra side impact protection.

The standard EEC crash test proved just how well Metro protects passengers.

Regulations state that in such a test the rearward

movement of the steering column must not exceed 5 inches.

The steering column in the Metro which hit a brick wall at 30MPH moved less than ¾ of an inch.

YOU WON'T BUY A METRO JUST BECAUSE IT'S BRITISH.

All 5 Metros are very well equipped.

The Metro L features a rear wash/wipe, heated rear windscreen, and, of course, the Split-Action seat.

The HLE may be economical, but it only skimps on petrol.

A quartz electric clock, cigar lighter and styled Halogen headlamps all add comfort to economy.

The sporty 1.3S is fashion-designer styled inside and out: double coachlines, special multi-tone upholstery, tinted glass and a push-button radio are standard.

And in the top-of-the-range HLS thick velour upholstery, head restraints and a lockable fuel filler cap add to an already formidable list of features.

THIS COULD BE YOUR FINEST HOUR.

A visit to your Austin Morris dealer will leave you surprised and impressed.

Surprised by prices, which begin at £3095, and impressed by the car.

Sit in the front and feel the comfort of the contoured seats. Sit in the back and feel the roominess. Then put the car through its paces on a test drive.

You'll find that at high speed it tracks straight as an arrow and takes bends like the white line in the middle of the road.

Then look at the back. Fold one seat down. Then the other. Look at all the load-carrying space. And if the boot fits, buy it.

AUSTIN 🇬🇧
with Supercover

METRO
A BRITISH CAR TO BEAT THE WORLD.

utterances, bowdlerise famous remarks, or habits, then use them to sell the Metro on a 'Buy British' campaign. The entire scene, or theme, was set by the very first 'teaser' ads, which showed a Metro completely swathed in a Union Jack, with the punchline: 'This could be your finest hour'.

There were quotations from Shakespeare, and Winston Churchill, and references to Britain's military heroes. It was a truly sentimental approach—but it worked. There was the reference to fuel economy: 'Never before have so many gone so far on so little'—and to the extended service intervals: 'Metro rules the bays'.

References to Lord Nelson and the Duke of Wellington both made their point: 'Metro, a fleet Nelson would have given his right arm for . . .' and 'Even Wellington never imagined a boot this big'. The wierdest pun of all, which drew attention to the very versatile seating was: 'To sit or not to sit? That is the question.'

All these, of course, were forceful enough, but there was only one display—a late addition, in fact—which led to controversy. Following the AA's test of an HLE, and the publication of their 83 mpg fuel economy figure at a steady 30 mph, BL rushed through a very simple, and very strong message. There in a simple picture, was a Metro, and under it were the simple and quite unambiguous words: 'The 83 mpg Metro'. Underneath it, in much smaller type, the message was spelt out more clearly: 'The new Austin Metro is designed to sip where others gulp. At a recent independent test performed by AA engineers, the Metro HLE achieved a remarkable

Below *To sit, or not to sit . . . was the question posed in some BL Metro adverts which ran this composite shot of the different rear seat folding arrangements. The off-centre split in the divided backrest was a minor stroke of genius.* **Right** *The controversial '83 mpg' advert, soon withdrawn. But BL Cars had already made their point by then . . ..*

 mini **METRO**   FOUR OF THE MANY VARIATIONS ON THE METRO REAR SEATING DESIGN

THE 83 MPG METRO.

The new Austin Metro is designed to sip where others gulp.

At a recent independent test performed by AA engineers, the Metro HLE achieved a remarkable 62MPG at a steady 50MPH.

At a steady 30MPH its results were nothing less than astounding: 83MPG.

Petrol economy like that is a product of aerodynamic body design and an engine that's been developed with tomorrow's fuel prices in mind.

Beneath Metro's sloping bonnet is the new A-Plus engine.

With its refined, positive gear box it has learned how to drive almost without drinking.

So even the sporty 1.3S and the luxurious 1.3HLS (96.5MPH, 0-60MPH in 12.3 seconds) get over 50MPG on the open road.

And to allow you to get full mileage from those figures, Metros are also designed to go 12,000 miles or one full year without a service.

So when the best hatchbacks the rest of the world has to offer have stopped for a service every 5000 or 6000 miles, you'll still keep going.

You'll go smoothly, too, with specially developed Hydragas suspension. And quietly.

Metro had quietness built into its design from the beginning using a structural vibrational analysis in an anechoic (echo-free) chamber.

Metro also has an asymmetric Split-Action rear seat to let you carry various combinations of passengers and luggage, all at the same time.

Metros start from £3095. You can start by booking a test drive. It could be your finest hour.

AUSTIN
METRO
A BRITISH CAR TO BEAT THE WORLD.

62 mpg at a steady 50 mph. At a steady 30 mph its results were nothing less than astounding: 83 mpg'.

Predictably, BL's competitors were insensed by this, for they thought that the headline was misleading. It suggested, they said, that any HLE owner could achieve 83 mpg in day-to-day motoring. There were complaints to the Advertising Standards Authority, and the result was that this particular advert was speedily withdrawn.

In retrospect, Tony Ball now agrees that the campaign might have been a misjudgement, but I also detected a cheerful gleam in his eyes while he was saying so: 'As to the 83 mpg at 30 mph—it was true enough. A fact is a fact. It *was* done. It

Somewhere in that scrum is BL's chairman, Sir Michael Edwardes (centre), World Champion Grand Prix driver Alan Jones, behind him, and sales chief Tony Ball, almost hidden by the camera flash equipment.

wasn't achieved by us. Having seen such an authoritative body as the AA say that this was so, we had to draw attention to it, didn't we?'.

The TV advertising, of course, claimed a huge audience, and the pugnacious 'white cliffs' campaign ran for weeks and weeks. BL were vastly amused, in the winter of 1981/1982 to see Alfa Romeo picking up the landing craft theme for themselves. In Alfa's case, their cars made a successful landfall . . ..

At NEC Motor Show time, the media—newspapers, radio and television companies—fell over themselves to cover the new Metro, and its arrival, in great and glorious detail. One rumour which spread like wildfire—and was speedily confirmed by BL's public relations staff—was that Sir Michael Edwardes was going to arrive at the NEC's exhibition halls in a Metro. Not only that, but he was to be chauffeured by the new World Champion motor racing driver, Alan Jones, whose Williams cars had been sponsored by Leyland Vehicles throughout the year.

One rumour was that Jones would drive Sir Michael all the way up the M1 from London, but this proved to be unfounded. One of my colleagues, in fact, was passed by Jones at high speed on the way to the show—but he was with team boss Frank Williams in the latter's sumptuous new Jaguar! The racing driver, in fact, met up with Sir Michael at the Metropole Hotel, which is quite close to the exhibition itself, and took the wheel at that point.

Their arrival at the main entrance, like that of royalty, was timed to the second, and their reception was fantastic. Fleet Street photographers, and all the agencies, had been primed for the occasion, and were out in force. The NEC had never seen anything like it. To have the world champion driving a Metro was quite a *coup de théâtre* in any case, but to have him chauffeuring BL's chairman was something else entirely It was quite out of the ordinary for a motor industry occasion—the amount of film exposed in the next few minutes would have gladdened the heart of a Kodak shareholder!

Inside the halls, it was almost impossible to get away from the Metro. The vast BL Cars stand not only had individual models on display, but had others on a special turntable, along with a special racing version intended for rallycross competition, and equipped with a special 16-valve cylinder head. All in all, there were 11 Metros on this stand alone.

But that was not all. *Autocar* were showing their 5,000-miles-in-five-days car, Lloyds Bank had one on show (of all things, for a bank, it was testing dampers!), while Ogle Design had already found time to do one of the splendid 'customised' Metros—the type which had so successfully been evolved on the basis of a Mini in previous years.

The Ogle Metro had actually been constructed by Wood & Pickett, the London-based coachbuilders also noted for their imaginative work on Range Rovers, and was placarded as the 'ultimate Metro'—even on the very first day the car was put on sale! Naturally it was kitted out in all the best of furnishings, which included electric

Sir Michael Edwardes expressing his delight to the cameramen, outside the NEC Motor Show on October 15 1980.

Above *The much-customised Ogle Metro, shown at the Motor Show in 1980, featuring special wheels, modified aerodynamic spoilers, and a much changed interior.* **Below** *The facia/ instrument panel of the Ogle Metro, to be produced to special order by Wood & Pickett of London* **Below right** *The 'bolt-on' turbocharger kit, developed by BL Motorsport for the 1980 Ogle Metro, was a portent of what BL themselves were planning for 1982.*

window lifts and central door locking, plus individual Recaro reclining seats, but there were many external changes, including the use of wheel arch extensions, spoilers, and side skirts, plus a new grille, Wolfrace alloy wide-rim wheels, and Pirelli P7 low-profile tyres.

There were so many visual changes in evidence that it was all too easy to miss the innovation in the engine bay. Prominent was a turbocharging installation, with a maximum blower 'boost' of 5 psi—it was a 'bolt-on' conversion developed by BL Cars' Special Tuning division at Abingdon, which was claimed to endow the little car with performance close to that of the V8-engined Rover 3500!

Ogle proposed to hand over production of this model to Wood & Pickett in London, where it was to be built under the generic name of 'Laser'. A faithful replica of the show car was priced at £12,000—at least three times that of the basic car— but the cost of individual examples would depend a lot on the type and level of furnishings chosen, and could vary from £8,000 to £15,000.

The most astonishing Metro of all (and, don't forget, this had been produced in advance of the car's public unveiling) was the rallycross prototype displayed on the BL Cars stand itself. It might look like a Metro, and indeed there were some Metro parts in it, but it was very different indeed under the skin.

Project Metro, as it was called, was a BL Motorsport/Unipart project, conforming to the RAC's 'silhouette' requirements for rallycross cars. Thus the body shape was almost pure Metro, though the 'chassis' was actually a tubular space frame developed by Safety Devices of East Anglia, and the lightweight body itself was constructed from glass fibre. A lightweight beam axle rear suspension replaced the Hydragas of the production car, the front suspension was by coil springs and double

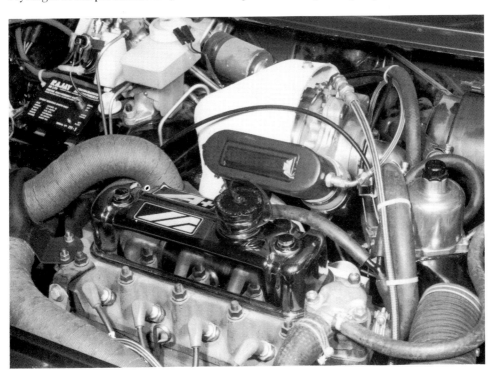

Above *That's cheating! A Dutch Metro, kitted out as a 'Politie' or police car.* **Below** *This was the very non-standard aspect of the engine shown in Project Metro, the BL-Unipart sponsored rallycross car, at the NEC Motor Show of 1980. The bottom end of the unit was pure BL A-Plus, but the cylinder head incorporated two overhead camshafts and four-valve combustion chambers.*

wishbones, and even the engine/transmission layout was vastly different. As shown at the NEC (but not actually as raced until mid-1981), the engine was a dramatic looking 1.5-litre unit, bored and stroked from the standard A-Plus cylinder block, but with a 16-valve twin-overhead-camshaft cylinder head, with belt drive to the cams, looking for all the world like a latter-day Bugatti, or a Ford BDA-clone.

Underneath this astonishing engine, which was said to produce nearly 200 bhp at 8,500 rpm, was what looked like a normal Metro front-wheel-drive transmission, but it actually hid a very robust gearbox and final drive by Jack Knight Transmissions, which incorporated a limited-slip differential. Much more of this car was to be heard of in 1981.

At the NEC Show itself, BL were delighted that so many prominent people should want to look at their new Metro, try it out for size, and have their pictures taken for posterity. In her rapid and typically forceful 'walkabout' on opening day, the Prime Minister, Mrs Margaret Thatcher, needed little encouragement to slip behind the wheel, and was anxious to emphasise how much public money *and* trust was riding on the back of the little car.

But the fantastic interest shown at the NEC motor show, and in all the newspapers immediately before launch, could not be self-sustaining. There was never much doubt that the Metro's initial sales record would be sensational, but the next few months were going to be a very worrying time for BL's management. Had it all been worthwhile? Would the general public continue to queue up to order Metros?

The portents, at least, were promising. Right at the start, the British School of Motoring put in a fleet order for 12,500 Metro Ls to be delivered to them over the next five years, and the first consignment was actually delivered to them before the Metro was officially announced. Later, to confirm that their choice had not merely been for patriotism, they announced that their in-service experience with the Metros had been more satisfactory than with any previous new model.

Professional road testers, national and regional, soon got their hands on the cars, and almost all of them were happy about the car. John Langley, in the *Daily Telegraph*, opened his report by saying something like: 'Ok, you can all relax. It's a jolly good little car'. Ruth Shelley, writing in the Watford *Evening Echo*, headlined her test: 'Yes, it's quite as good as they said it is'.

There were, however, several notes of caution. *Autocar*, who did not rush a test into print, but carried out their usual lengthy appraisal, said of their 1.3HLS: 'Excellent—but could easily be still better'. A Peterborough paper, too, asked: 'Can the Austin Metro survive all that BL ballyhoo?', though this wasn't really fair as most of the ballyhoo came from the media men themselves. Clive Jacobs, writing soon after the release, asked: 'Was it a carefully orchestrated sales campaign, or just the best example of the worst-kept secret? Anyway, I cannot recall any new car getting so much publicity either before or after its official launch'.

Perhaps the most useful, but accidental, publicity *coup* of all came in November when a shy young lady working at a kindergarten in West London took delivery of a Metro for herself. Her name was Lady Diana Spencer, and at the time her name was being linked with HRH Prince Charles, the heir to the British throne, in a purely speculative manner. For once, however, Fleet Street's scandal-mongers were proved right, for the young lady became the Princess of Wales in July 1981. Unfortunately, she is not now seen in a Metro . . . .

Many people, incidentally, had tried to scrounge cars from BL to carry out Metro 'stunts', but most were refused. CI Caravans, Britain's largest manufacturers,

Above *Britain's Prime Minister, Mrs Margaret Thatcher, and Denis Thatcher, posing with a Metro at the 1980 NEC Motor Show.* **Below** *Mrs Thatcher could not suppress her delight at the way the Metro was being received, when she visited the BL stand.* **Opposite** *HRH Prince Michael of Kent, himself a keen sporting motorist, was one of the first to try the Metro for size, and be briefed about its equipment.*

John Mantle and Brendan Witter at John o'Groats at the conclusion of their record breaking 46.3 mph average speed drive from Land's End, with a 12 foot CI Caravans Sprite Alpine in tow.

however, were able to borrow a 1.3HLS, and soon set up a notable 'record'. Driven by John Mantle and Brendan Witter, the Metro 1.3HLS towed a 12 foot CI Caravans Sprite Alpine from Lands End to John O'Groats in 18 hours 58 minutes. The distance was 876 miles, and the average speed set was 46.3 mph—not bad considering that the legal speed limit for towing a caravan in Britain is 50 mph.

At the NEC Motor Show, the Metro had picked up two Gold medals in the IBCAM Coachwork competition, and it was this sort of instant reputation for quality which helped get the customers into the showrooms. With production already building up beyond 3,000 cars a week (all for the domestic market—sales to Europe would not begin until April 1981), there was no shortage of supply. In the car's first full sales month, November 1980, 6,881 Metros were sold, which instantly gave it 7.5 per cent of the market. Only the Escorts and Cortinas, as expected, outsold it, and the Fiesta was left trailing, 1,200 cars behind.

It was just the start which the Metro needed, for BL was never clear of controversy, and industrial matters at Longbridge were still providing their fair share of headlines for the newspapers. In particular, the workforce was still being slimmed down, work rates were going up all the time (as was productivity) and the company's annual wage round was being negotiated. During 1980, the BL Cars workforce had been reduced from 85,400 to 64,300, mainly (but not entirely) by factory closures and enforced redundancies and management were determined to keep the new Metro production lines going at all costs to make sure that no further slimming-down of the Longbridge workforce would be needed.

Large losses were still being incurred by BL as Sir Michael Edwardes' 'Recovery Plan' continued to be carried out, and one result was that for the third year in succession only a small offer of increase had been made to hourly-paid workers before the November 1st deadline, one which was well below the prevailing level of inflation. In this sort of atmosphere there was bound to be a flashpoint somewhere, and it duly erupted on November 21, when 500 trim workers at Longbridge were laid off during a dispute over the supply of Metro seats from outside suppliers.

To quote the *Daily Mail*, the following morning: 'Scores of frustrated Metro car workers ran riot through BL's Longbridge plant yesterday after learning they were to be laid off. Frightened clerical workers barricaded themselves in their offices as the workers chanted, ''We want to work'', broke windows and doors . . . On the factory floor, pallets of components were overturned and unfinished Metros slightly damaged'.

The problem, and its causes, was not simple to analyse, for it involved all the factors already mentioned. Whatever the rights and wrongs of the dispute, it damaged Longbridge's reputation at a time when serenity and goodwill were ideally needed. In the end, not only were the 'bought out' seats fitted to seatless Metros waiting for them, but a few members of the workforce were disciplined, fined, or even sacked for the damage and disruption caused. In the end, too, the

Sales chief, Tony Ball, handing over a Metro to the Welsh Rugby Union (note the appropriate registration number), with two famous players, Steve Fenwick and Gerald Davies, on the other side of the car.

company's final pay offer of a 6.8 per cent basic increase, allied to improved bonus conditions, was accepted and things returned, somewhat uneasily, to normal.

Fortunately the Metro soon found its feet, even though the range was not yet complete, nor likely to be so for some time. BL's market researchers had done their job well, for there was no shortage of potential customers for the cars. Mass interviews showed that hatchback purchases were governed by major factors like fuel economy, boot space, price and value for money, exterior style and small size—all of which the Metro had in excellent profusion.

More important, however, was the way that the market for two-door saloons or three-door hatchbacks had changed during the 1970s. In the 'small' (but not 'mini') car field, the sales of three-door cars had expanded enormously throughout, but did not overtake those of two-door saloons before 1977, three years after development of the Metro had begun. By the end of 1979, when it was physically, financially and practically impossible to alter the design of the new BL baby, three-doors outsold two-doors by a factor of three to two.

In any case, the entire 'small-car' market itself was still increasing steadily. In 1972, in the 'Year of the Renault 5', small cars took only 11 per cent of the British market, but by 1979 their share had risen to no less than 16 per cent. BL, and their rivals, were predicting that this would rise again, to at least 18 per cent, by 1981, and this was *before* the massive rise in petrol prices, sparked off by the change in crude oil prices in 1979, had been able to take their effect.

BL's biggest worry, stated or otherwise, was the new front-wheel-drive Escort. Even though its launch had been strangely muted in the UK (there were even some suggestions that Ford handed the limelight to BL because the nationalised British 'underdog' would always win the day on sentimental grounds), it had been very well-received in Europe. The Escort was put into production in Britain (at Halewood) and in West Germany, and was put on sale in most European countries right from the start.

BL were not ready to put the Metro into Europe until they had satisfied the initial demand in Britain, and until both the new fully-automated body and assembly lines had been opened up, so the Escort gobbled up a lot of hatchback sales in the winter months. The fact that it was, in marketing terms, half a size larger than the Metro didn't matter to the casual public, or to the newspapers, and the fact that the Escort won the prestigious Car of the Year award for 1981 didn't help either.

In Britain, however, the Escort's initial boom was short-lived, for it began to run into some production problems with the new machinery (advanced, but not as automated as that installed at Longbridge), and then it suffered somewhat from a spate of strikes at Halewood. Its image was not helped either when Ford's new chief executive, Sam Toy, complained publicly that the car was not being produced so efficiently in Britain as it was in West Germany.

As it happened, the Metro did not seem to need any acts of God, or large slices of good luck, to make its way in the world. Most of the initial media praise seemed to roll on, and on, and even the more cynical publications found little to carp about. *Motoring Which*, who had bought a Metro 1.0L as soon as they could, were rather waspish about the AA's '83 mpg at 30 mph' fuel consumption figures: 'It's patently absurd to suggest that an ordinary motorist will get anything like this consumption and detracts, in every day terms, from what is an economical car'. In the first 2,000 miles recorded by their car, they had clocked up 39 mpg.

Autocar didn't get their hands on a 1.0-litre Metro until April 1981, nearly six months after launch, and this was not the super-economical HLE version, but they said that the car had a 'remarkable blend of performance with economy', and suggested that in gentle driving, day to day, an owner ought to be able to beat 45 mpg, though their own (hard-driven) figure was only 35.2 mpg. Their own Metro HLE did not behave well at first, principally there were problems with the carburation, but by the time the 12,000 mile mark was being reached early in 1982, the engine recorded 73.3 mpg at 30 mph, and 55.4 mpg at 50 mph.

Quite suddenly, however, a new Metro became *the* car to have in this country, not only to show that one was economy-conscious, but that one was also patriotic. The first 56,000 Metros were sold in six months from introduction, a build up almost unprecedented in BL's history. Moreover, not only was the car consistently winning more than the six per cent of the British market originally forecast for it, but the Mini's sales were holding up remarkably well. For the first time in years, analysts could see BL's UK market share rising, and they were actually selling more cars in 1981 than in 1980, at a time when Britain's economy was moving smartly into recession, and sales as a whole were on the way down. In some early months, combined Metro and Mini sales exceeded 10 per cent, a statistic which brought smiles to every face except those of the Metro's rivals. The Fiesta, however, stood up very well to this onslaught, especially when the 'Popular' version was introduced during 1981.

In the spring of 1981, however, the Metro's first (and, thankfully, only) setback occurred. Within days, two complaints were received that Metro steering mechanisms had locked up. Was this serious, or was it a repeat of the famous 'Mini drive shaft breakage' scare of a few years earlier?

There were two reports—one from a lady driver, the other from a man with a surgical boot—both said that they had found their 'clutch' foot tight up against the steering column, and that the steering had stiffened right up. Somehow or other, this news was leaked to *The Guardian* newspaper, and published as a major scandal. There was instant uproar and questions were even asked in Parliament.

Harold Musgrove can now smile about the incident, for there was a simple solution, but he admits that the implications worried him deeply for a time. 'There was an immense rumpus', he told me, 'and we had to investigate it at once. I actually borrowed a Metro, and tried to reproduce the problem, but couldn't even identify it. In the end I called in Charles Maple, our director of Quality Audit, and asked him for advice, and it wasn't for an hour or so that he could find anyone to make it happen to their Metro.'

In certain circumstances, it seems, it was possible for a shoe to distort the rubber gaiter at the bottom of the steering column, and to have it catch the exposed thread of a nut clamping the column to the steering rack. In time the thread could cut the rubber, and in time the rubber could catch behind the nut—*then* it was that the steering stiffened up. 'But it was a very contrived problem—very obscure', Musgrove said. 'What did we do? We just reversed the fixing of the nut and bolt . . . end of story!'

In the meantime, the Metro continued to beat every target, and set new ones for itself. Production had restarted after the Christmas 1980 break at 3,500 Metros a week, and was soon pushed up to 4,500 or even 4,700 a week in the spring. Soon the Metro represented 50 per cent of *all* Austin-Morris sales, and BL Cars' overall market share was up about 20 per cent again, and staying there. About three in

In 1981 the British Guild of Motoring Writers made the Metro their Top Car of the year. Here, at the awards ceremony, are Ray Horrocks (left, chairman and chief executive of BL Cars), shaking hands with Tony Ball (chairman and managing director of BL Europe & Overseas).

every four Metro sales were of the most economical 1.0-litre version, with the 1.0L selling best of all.

The list of awards it had won continued to mount up. *What Car* dubbed it the 'Best Small Car' of 1981, and the influential British Guild of Motoring Writers made it their Top Car of the Year. It also won the Duke of Edinburgh's design award, and the Design Council award. The two most prestigious awards, however, were yet to come. In April 1981 the design was given the Don Trophy, an accolade for its many safety features, and later it was also awarded the RAC's Dewar Trophy, which is only given for what is considered to be an outstanding motor industry achievement.

Before long, the only thing which was holding the Metro back at all was the lack of enough cars to sell, and—to a degree—the lack of an automatic transmission option. Tony Ball reckons that many more Metros could have been sold to British customers if they had been available. Tony Ball maintained, in 1981, that the Metro could have won four to five per cent more of the British market if cars had not had to be diverted to Europe. But the European market needed attention—for BL sales had been falling away in recent years—and the Metro looked likely to be the car to spearhead the revival. In the 1960s, the Mini had flourished bravely in France, Italy and other European countries. Now, in 1981, 20 years later, it was the Metro's turn to do the same.

Automatic transmission, which was still not available on the Metro's major rivals, had been optional on Minis since 1965. It was not available on the Metro from the start, purely because Harold Musgrove and Tony Ball realised that they could not tackle everything all at once.

'Rather than launch it at half-cock, I'd rather wait until we'd got it available in numbers—and that wasn't in October 1980', Tony Ball insisted. 'We waited until the first summer, and then pushed through the first Metro automatics. Building is supply-constrained to a degree, but now we manage to sell about eight per cent of all Metros with automatic transmission.' But that represents only 400 Metro automatics a week. Is it profitable? 'Yes it is. *Everything* we do today has to be commercially and financially viable.'

The miracle was that there wasn't such a price penalty as people were expecting. The new derivative was presented as a Metro Automatic, a separate version of the car, and it was not strictly comparable with any other Metro. The result was that although there were some features of the 1.3HLS's trim and furnishings in the Automatic, which shared exactly the same engine, it initially cost £4,595, £52 *less* than that of the manual 1.3HLS.

The transmission itself was a developed version of the Automotive Products four-speed unit which had been used in Minis, 1100/1300s and Allegro models for some years and was linked to very high overall gearing, so that the car was claimed to be

The 100,000th Metro to be built at Longbridge, in the summer of 1981, with Austin-Morris chairman Harold Musgrove (left) watching the ceremony. There will be many more celebrations and milestones like this.

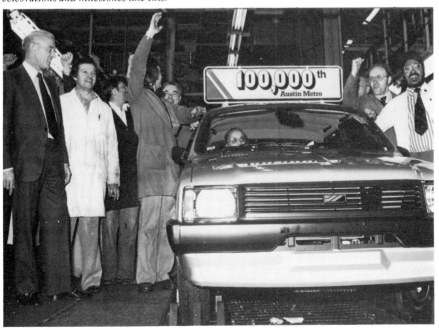

more economical than cars like the manual-transmission Fiesta, if not quite as miserly as the manual Metros themselves.

In such a busy year as this, it would have been easy for BL to rely purely on retail and fleet sales to spell out the Metro's success, but the marketing operation did not stop there. The Project Metro rallycross car which appeared at the NEC Motor Show finally made its debut in April 1981 and, after a redesign of the front suspension to a strut layout, began to win classes against the Fiestas, which had already been competing for a couple of years, and had received much more detail development.

BL Motorsport also gave their support to two Metros being used in the 1981 Tricentrol RAC British Saloon Car Championship, and there was a self-contained Unipart-sponsored Metro Racing Challenge series as well. The two 'works-supported' Group 1 Metros were driven by Richard Longman and Alan Curnow, and had started life as 1.3S derivatives. By the time Longman's Dorset-based workshops had finished with the car, it was carrying distinctive Datapost livery, was powered by a 115 bhp engine using Weber carburation, and was very rapid indeed. It was asking too much for this car to be competitive right away, but the two cars nevertheless managed to finish second and third in their capacity class. Great things were expected for the cars' second season, when they were to run to a new Post-Office-red colour scheme.

One result of Tony Ball's barnstorming and almost evangelic approach to selling BL Cars, and the new Metro, was that the slow and dispiriting loss of BL dealerships in the UK was halted. Perhaps for the first time since the early 1970s, when a rationalisation of the network was started (fewer, larger, outlets, it was said, was the way to go—it was a policy with which many marketing men did not agree), there were motor traders queueing up to take on the franchises.

'Soon after I came back to BL, in 1978', Tony Ball told me, 'I introduced a rural dealer recruitment programme. I made it clear not only that I wanted to halt the drop in market share we had been suffering, but I wanted to increase the dealer chain again. Before I arrived, the number of outlets had been reduced from about 5,000 to 2,000 in this country alone—mainly by weeding out individual Austin and Morris outlets in one town. Now, following the success of Metro, and of course cars like the Acclaim, and the revised Rovers and Princesses (Ambassadors), we're processing lots of applications for new BL dealerships—more than 400 in 1981 alone.'

Even before it reached the end of its first year on the market, the Metro had become a familiar part of the British and European motoring scene. Even though the sales and marketing staffs had to look after the launch of other new BL models, notably the Triumph Acclaim (which was the slightly redesigned Honda Ballade, built under licence by BL at the Cowley factory), they had time to reflect on the Metro's successes, and how it was to be improved and made more attractive, for the future.

On its first birthday, in October 1981, the statistics began to roll out of BL's publicity machine. In the first 12 months, more than 122,000 Metros had been sold, and had made retail sales exceeding £500 million. Production was running at 4,600 cars a week at Longbridge, where the Metro out-numbered the long-established Minis and Allegros completely, and its established UK market share was now eight per cent.

At the end of 1981 itself, BL's calendar year figures were even more impressive. In 1981 alone, 165,745 Metros had been assembled, compared with 49,190 Minis and 22,908 Allegros, and all this had helped to transform BL Cars' prospects. In a

Above *Spot the difference? The special quadrant on the floor shows that this is one of the first Metro Automatics, now making up about 8 per cent of production* **Below** *The only way to 'pick' an automatic-transmission Metro is by reading the badging on the rear hatch.*

particularly grim trading year, when the British economy sank further and further into depression, BL Cars was the only major car-maker not only to increase its market share, but to increase the number of cars built and sold in a declining market.

Tony Ball was not only speaking for himself, but for the whole of BL, when he said, in a New Year message: 'The Metro symbolises the pride we all feel for British industry. It has captured the hearts of the public and made an impact beyond that even expected from those of us who knew the car would be a best seller . . . The Metro is the most exciting and important saloon car to be designed and made in Britain for over a decade'.

It might have been slight hyperbole, and excusable in view of the way that BL Cars' prospects had been transformed in recent months, but it was a view shared by many owners. By this time, a familiar sight in the rear window of Metros was a proud sticker proclaiming: 'I love my Metro', in which the 'love' was in the shape of a heart!

It was, however, asking too much for all the new working pressures at Longbridge to have been absorbed completely, and passively. The workforce at Longbridge was still being cut back, as production of the Allegro gradually tailed away, and industrial peace was disturbed in October 1981 (at around 'first birthday time') by the annual wage round negotiations.

The BL Group was still suffering heavy losses, due to massive investment in new equipment, the closure of factories, and the general recession in world markets. The annual loss in 1980 had been more than £500 million, and it was not expected to be cut by much in the next 12 months. Even though Sir Michael Edwardes and Ray Horrocks were now confidently forecasting that BL Cars would break even in 1983, and move firmly into profit in 1984, there was little money available for wage increases in 1981.

The result was that when management made an offer of only 3.8 per cent on basic rates, and coupled it with improved bonus terms, the trade unions, led by Grenville Hawley of the TGWU, were most unhappy. At first there was no sign of a settlement, and no sign of an improved management offer. An all-out strike was called, and indeed paralysed Longbridge for a few days towards the end of the year, but Sir Michael Edwardes made it clear that no more money would be forthcoming, and that he was quite prepared to recommend liquidation of BL Cars, and abandonment of the recovery programme, if the offer was not accepted.

Emotional scenes followed at various mass meetings before the workforce decided, however reluctantly, to return to work and accept the offer. Although it was not a happy time, for men or for management, it was at last possible to see signs of improvement in the business, both at Longbridge (where the Metro was being built), and at Cowley, which would have a total of three new models on stream by the spring of 1982. Not only was the Metro a success, but it was still selling as fast as it could be built. Better than this, was the promise of exciting developments in the near future. New models, and new derivatives, of the Metro were already on the way.

Chapter 9

New models for new markets
The latest derivatives

Many years ago, it was possible for a new car to be produced, for no further derivatives to be made available and for everyone to be happy; it was often profitable to do so. But that *was* all a long time ago. There was never any question of the Metro merely being an Austin, or merely looking like the first cars to meet their public. Let's never forget that even the legendary Model T Ford came in a whole variety of different body styles, and that, in its time, there have been an astonishing number of derivatives of the ubiquitous VW Beetle.

In Britain, perhaps, although it was the Rootes Group which first adopted 'badge engineering', it was the forerunner of BL Cars, BMC, which raised the process to something of a fine art in the 1960s. But there are vast differences between 'badge engineering' and the provision of a complete and integrated range. 'Badge engineering' refers to the minor changes made to one basic design with no more than decoration and trim to pinpoint the differences. The provision of a complete range—of engines, trim packs, body styles and mechanical types—is more subtle and infinitely more honest.

BMC's 'badge engineering' excesses were soon over and cars like the Minis and the 1100/1300s were eventually built in several guises, each with its own marketing niche in view. By the 1970s, when planning for the new 'Supermini', the ADO88, got under way, it was quite usual for a British manufacturer to plan in this way.

Developing many cars based on the Mini had been wonderfully successful, though by the rantings of some media outlets one would think that it was a crime to do so. There should surely have been no complaints when such a policy not only resulted in extra profit for the manufacturer, but extra demand from the paying customer? Big business, after all, should look to its sales, rather than to its cosmetic image with the media. Perhaps the Mini range had become too complicated and more so than the Metro was ever likely to be. There had, after all, been more than a dozen recognisably different types—Austins, Morrises, Rileys and Wolseleys, normal saloons, booted saloons (so what was new about the VW Derby, after all?), vans, pick-ups, estate cars and open-to-all-weathers Mokes. There had also been a multitude of engine sizes, power outputs, a choice of transmissions and different nose stylings. The fact is, however, that of the first 4.5 million Minis to be built, no more than three million were normal-shape Austin/Morris saloons—there had been consider-able virtue, therefore, in providing all the alternatives.

Naturally, none of this escaped the attention of the product planners. They thought the Mini range too complex (and, from the beginning of the 1970s,

Above *There are slight decorative differences between the Metro 1.3S and* **(above right)** *the Metro 1.3HLS, but you have to search hard to find them.* **Right** *Some versions of the Metro have podded, rather than flush-mounted headlamps. This was the original Metro 1.0L.*

gradually cut it back), but they were always planning to offer an integrated range of new 'Superminis', In January 1976, when the style of ADO88 was agreed, the precedent was still there, in Leyland Cars' price lists, for all to see. There were still five Mini private cars, plus the vans and pick-ups. There were also nine Allegros with Austin badges, plus the up-market Vanden Plas Princess derivative as well.

Steve Schlemmer, who arrived in the department in 1977, recalls that: 'At first, we merely thought of a range of Austins, up to and including HLS models. Once we had settled the basics of these, we started to think of sporting and Vanden Plas derivatives at the beginning of 1979. The turbo and the City types came on the scene later. We soon realised that the car had great potential, in 'down-sizing' terms, to draw custom down to it. On that basis, a Vanden Plas type of Metro was worth doing, and it's always been a profitable version to build'.

Planning for such cars had not progressed very far in 1979 when the second massive wave of oil prices began to have a serious effect (the first wave had come in 1973/1974). Not only did the price of petrol itself go through the roof, but the economics of entire nations began to be affected and living standards began to slip.

Although that was bad news for many car makers, it was actually rather good news for BL Cars, who were predominantly making smaller vehicles. The rises in petrol costs and the increase in unemployment which began to spread around Europe, made the concept of a well-equipped, well-trimmed, Metro more attractive and more suitable for many people. It needed very little analysis to prove that there was going to be a more marked process of 'trading-down' or 'down-sizing' in the

years to come. Accordingly, this meant that many motorists who had previously bought medium-sized cars with a certain degree of style, equipment and performance, would be looking for the same creature comforts and behaviour, in more fuel-efficient smaller cars in the 1980s.

The slump in economic activity was so marked that the car market itself began to change quite quickly, with a new accent not only on small cars, but on small, cheap and *very* economical cars. Thus it was that the more sporty, up-market, Metro derivatives already taking shape at Longbridge had to be shunted briefly aside, to allow two other types of Metro to be produced, one for France only, and one primarily for Britain.

In France, the Metro was very well received when it was launched there in the spring of 1981, but the importers soon pointed out a particular fiscal loophole in that country, and asked if a Metro derivative could be made available to match it. In effect, a private car could still look like a private car, but if it was modified so that no rear seat was fitted (and no rear seat *could* be fitted) then it would rank as a commercial vehicle, and attract important tax concessions. Clearly this was only attractive to companies making hatchback cars, and was a category and market Citroën and Renault had been serving for some years.

The result was that, in double-quick time, BL modified the cheapest type of Metro, with the 1.0-litre engine, took out the rear seat and the versatile folding mechanisms and substituted a flat, carpet-covered, wooden shelf between the rear of the unchanged front seats and the hatchback door itself. The result was the Metro Commerciale which was being made in considerable numbers early in 1982.

The other evolution was more obvious, and had several noted precedents. Ford had started the whole thing off in 1975 with their Escort Popular, and BL had carried it forward in 1979 with the Mini City. In short, the strategy was to take an existing design, endow it with the most economical possible engine, strip out as little equipment as possible, but then reduce its selling price by as much as possible and introduce it as the bottom-of-the-range version. In almost every case, such cars have proved to be very popular in recession-hit Great Britain, and they are *never* 'loss-leaders'.

BL Cars, in fact, had not originally planned to produce such a Metro, but the successful launch of Ford's Fiesta Popular (an obvious, and very direct competitor for Metro sales) made it almost inevitable. In the bad old days of British Leyland, before the atmosphere of battle had truly taken hold of the vitals of management, it would have taken time to bring this about, but not any more. 'We took the decision to produce a Metro City', Steve Schlemmer told me, 'in September or October 1981 and we decided to launch it in February 1982. The whole process took a mere five months. The final touches on styling—badges, and so on—plus equipment were taken in November 1981 and we had the car in production, in volume, on the track, in February 1982. We *have* to think quickly in today's industrial climate, and in this case we did!'

When it was launched, BL described the Metro City as 'budget-priced', which it

Opposite top *A Metro engine bay, in fact of a left-hand drive derivative. The cooling radiator is tucked away under the front cross panel.* **Bottom** *Ample space in the rear seat and that' splendidly versatile folding arrangement. The rear-seat belts are not standard on British Metros.*

certainly was, but it was encouraging to see that, compared with the original 'base' Metro there had been very little reduction in standard equipment. Compared with the 'base' Metro, the only major pieces of equipment not fitted to the City were the radio, and the wipe-wash feature for the rear hatchback window. Seat covering was in vinyl and, like the 'base' Metro, there was no split-folding arrangement of the rear seat.

In basic specification and equipment, therefore, the City lacked for little, but it was most certainly cheaper than before. At a time when prices in the Metro range started at £3,599, and went up to £4,948, the 1.0-litre Metro City looked a real bargain at a mere £3,250.

It was even more of a bargain when the price of the Mini 1000HL (£3,363), and major rival products like the Ford Fiesta Popular (£3,255), and the 850 cc Renault 5 (£3,367) were taken into consideration. BL were fairly confident when they announced that they expected the Metro City 'to take a UK market share of well over one per cent'—which meant that they were expecting to sell more than 15,000

Right The Metro City, launched in February 1982, was a successful attempt to stretch the Metro market even further down the price tables, and to meet the opposition head on. Compared with other 1.0-litre Metros, the only major omissions of equipment were the radio and the rear window wipe-wash equipment. **Below right** *Metro City means a 1.0-litre Metro, shorn of only a little equipment, selling for a mere £3,250 (£349 less than the ordinary 'base' Metro) in the spring of 1982.* **Below** *John Cooper, of Cooper-Mini fame, now a BL dealer in Sussex, started marketing this specially tuned and modified Metro in 1982. At first it was to be called a Cooper-Metro, and it was hoped to keep the full guarantee offered by the factory, but its final name was 'Monaco'.*

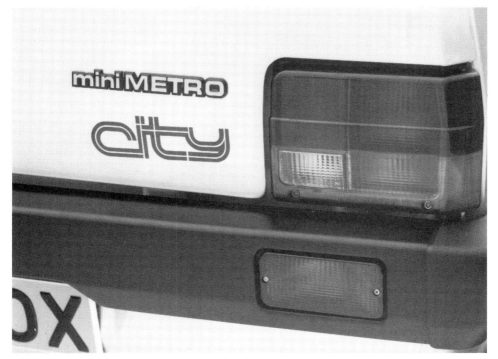

of these no-frills cars in a full year.

In the meantime, before BL could finalise work on their own more up-market Metros, several significant derivatives of the basic design had been put on the market by private concerns. One of them had a most charismatic and 'classic' name— 'Metro-Cooper'—while another was bidding for the instant title of 'Ultimate Metro', for it carried a £12,000 price tag.

In many ways the Metro Cooper was the spiritual *and* the actual successor to the well-loved Mini-Coopers of the 1960s. It was the spiritual successor because it was intended to be the same sort of small, nimble sports saloon, and because it was inspired by the same man—John Cooper, of Cooper Grand Prix car fame. In the 1960s, the Cooper and Cooper S models had done more for BMC's reputation than any amount of advertising could ever do, and in a rather different way John Cooper was hoping to repeat the success with a Metro-based car.

The difference was that this time there could be no direct factory link (this had been untied by Lord Stokes in the early 1970s). John Cooper had become a BL (Austin-Morris) dealer in Ferring, Sussex, and, in conjunction with the Wadham Stringer group of 32 BL dealerships, he was planning to market a new car, effectively a Metro 1.3 HLS, with modified engine, with Wolfrace light-alloy wheels and with different and distinctive paint schemes. At first it was hoped to retain the full factory warranty on the unmodified parts of the car, but BL Cars would not agree to this. Furthermore, there were 'trade mark' problems over the use of the 'Cooper' name in a car not sponsored by the factory, and the result was that the finalised product eventually became known as the Metro Monaco, the 'Monaco' title being a throwback to another famous Cooper competition car of the 1960s.

Whatever its name, however, John Cooper's little car had a great deal of performance as, with twin SU carburettors, a free-flow exhaust manifold, a raised compression ratio and a different camshaft, it ought to have had. *Autocar*'s test impressions were headlined 'Metro Ton Bomb', and they quoted a top speed of 101 mph, 0-60 mph in 11.6 seconds, and the sprint to a quarter mile, from rest, in 18.7 seconds. These were equal to the Mini-Cooper S with the 1,275 cc engine and turned the little car into a real road burner. It was, however, a performance level which BL thought they could match, without as much complication, and while naturally retaining their own warranty arrangements.

The 'ultimate Metro', the Frazer Tickford, was a product of the Tickford coachbuilding company, which is controlled by Aston-Martin-Lagonda, and took its name from the Frazer concern, who thought up the combination of features in the car. As announced in October 1981, it featured a different nose, front spoiler and side/tail styling, and carried the astonishing price tag of £11,608. At this price, incidentally, one could have bought a Rover 3500SE or even a fully-equipped Porsche 924!

The Frazer starts life as a Metro 1.3S, but as soon as Tickford have laid hands on it they gut the body shell, remove the engine and front suspension and start again! The bodies are all in high gloss silver, a colour which is subtly graded towards a darker shade as it nears the sills all around the car. There are obvious styling changes, by glass-fibre panelling, all of which is below the car's natural waistline. At the front there is a new combined front bumper cover and spoiler, rather in the Vauxhall Chevette HSR mould, allied to a two-slat grille to replace the standard item.

At the side, there are pronounced sills, almost 'running boards' (and again, very much like those fitted to the Chevette HSR rally car), while at the rear there is a new lower panel to match with the re-shaping of the front and sides of the car. The 1,275 cc engine has been further developed by Aston Martin Tickford engineers and, with a Weber 32/34 DMTL carburettor and a modified cylinder head, it is claimed to produce more than 80 bhp. The front suspension is re-tuned, and stiffened up, while a dramatic type of 13 inch cast-alloy road wheel by ARC of Germany was allied to very low profile 175/50VR 13 inch Pirelli P7 tyres.

But it is the inside of the Frazer Metro which is so obviously, and very sumptuously, different. There is a new facia, new instruments, new seats and many other details. The quality of the trim and furnishing is of a standard one would expect from a company which has links with a 'Supercar' firm like Aston Martin. Naturally, all glass is tinted, there are electrical window lifts and a laminated glass sun roof is standard. The floor covering is Wilton carpet, the seat coverings real leather and the roof lining is tweed cloth. It not only looks superb, but smells delightful. All in all, it is an amazing machine, the sort of car one could only look upon as an indulgence— and yet it seems to have found a limited market up to the expectations of Frazer. Sales got off in a rush after the launch but, by mid-1982, they had settled down so that production could go ahead steadily at the rate of about four to six cars a month.

In this respect, it is interesting to hear that Wood and Pickett found that few customers wanted all the coachbuilt items in the Ogle-inspired car, the Laser, as shown at the NEC Motor Show of 1980, but that most were interested in the engine improvements (particularly turbocharging) and the changes to the facia and the seats. This, when one thinks about it, is a wonderful tribute to the mass-production standards achieved in the Metro as built in large numbers at Longbridge.

In April and May 1982, however, BL Cars finally revealed their own up-market derivatives, producing two new Metros, one called an MG, and the other called a Vanden Plas. Mechanically, in fact, there were subtle but clever changes, to match the obvious style improvements, but the rationale behind these cars is fascinating.

Although there was something of an outcry from died-in-the-wool MG traditionalists when it became known that there was to be an 'MG' Metro, there are many precedents for the marketing of such a car. Although there never was an MG Mini, it is not generally known that such a car might have been produced, if the Mini-Cooper and Mini-Cooper S had not done the same sort of image-boosting operation while carrying Austin and Morris badges. There had been MG saloon cars in the past, some with pedigree, some with very little. Once again, to the chagrin of MG traditionalists, those with less pedigree appear to have sold much more strongly than their more specialised brethren. In particular, the MG1100 and MG1300 versions of the Austin/Morris 1100/1300 models were extremely popular. Between 1962 and 1971, no fewer than 143,000 of all types were built.

It is idle to wonder why an increased-performance Metro was not called a Metro-Cooper, to bring it historically into line with the Mini-Cooper, though I suspect one reason would be that this would have linked the Metro with John Cooper, who had nothing to do with the development of the new factory-designed derivatives, and it might even have meant BL paying royalties under an old agreement! BL Cars, for all the obvious reasons, decided to call their first proper sporting Metro by one of the corporation's sporting names. The choice, presumably, would have been between MG and Triumph, and MG won out in the end.

Before going on to describe the changes made to the basic design, it is important that I should recall what the MG fraternity thought about this when they first heard of it. Initially, of course, there had been fury at the idea of a non-MG car having MG

The MG Metro's interior has contoured, figure-hugging seats, a padded-leather steering wheel and special instrument styling, not forgetting the floor carpets which are bright red.

identity given to it, but this attitude was substantially modified when there had been time for thought to prevail.

Bill Wallis, chairman of the MG Car Club, the longest-established of all MG enthusiast clubs, was in no doubt: 'In the MG Car Club we want to see the name maintained. We might have preferred a GT coupé, or an open sports car, but they can come later. If the name is allowed to die, *nothing* can come later . . . surely we all agree that the name should live on, provided that the car that carries it is good. A crisp, well set-up, quick Mini Metro could be very good. If such a model were to be produced, its owners would be very welcome to join our ranks'. It might have been a bit of adroit advertising for the club, but it also recognised the realities of the MG situation. The MGB, after all, had died on its feet in 1980, and there were still unsold examples washing around the motor trade in 1982.

BL, however, were fully aware of the situation. In the 1960s, for sure, they would have ploughed on and ignored the attitudes of MG enthusiasts but, in the 1980s, they wanted to do the right thing. In an unprecedented move, both Wallis and Roche

Below *MG motoring, 1982 style, with the MG Metro 1300—72 bhp and 100 mph-plus performance. The glass sunroof on this particular car is an optional extra.* **Below right** *To improve the already good aerodynamics of the Metro for the MG version, BL engineers developed this horseshoe-shaped spoiler around the top of the tailgate, which reduces the drag coefficient from 0.41 to 0.39, a gain of five per cent.*

Bentley, chairman of the other (and larger) MG club, the MG Owners Club, were both invited to Longbridge some months before the car was ready to go on sale, ushered into the styling studios, and asked for their opinion of what was proposed.

As a result of this, some visual changes were made, which emphasised the MG aspect of the car even more than had been done before. 'It was after talking to Bill and Roche', Steve Schlemmer says, 'that we finally decided to fit the side striping, which is such an obvious recognition feature. Up to then, we had not finally made up our minds, but the attitude of the two chairmen convinced us that it would be acceptable. Incidentally, at one point we had even considered fitting octagonal instruments, like some old MG saloon cars had had, but it just didn't look right, somehow.' There were other, and more minor changes, none of which significantly changed the character of the car.

In preparing the MG version of the Metro, the object was to give the car a performance equal to that of the much-loved Mini-Cooper S of the 1960s with road-holding to match and a better standard of trim and finish than any previous BMC/BL MG saloon car, but to keep costs within bounds. That, and the implications of making changes to the body shell 'sheet metal' in the New West Works at Longbridge, meant that the MG would basically be the same as the other Metros when viewed from the outside, but that there could be many decorative ways of making it stand out.

The real breakthrough came in the wind tunnel, where an entirely new type of

rear spoiler was developed. This, finished in black plastic, is bolted to the hatchback, and lifts with it. However, it is not a simple roof top 'flip', but takes the shape of a horseshoe and almost encircles the glass of the hatchback. Several different shapes and sizes were tried at the prototype stage—that finally chosen is effective and looks neat.

The aerodynamic drag coefficient of the standard Metro is 0.41 but, with the rear spoiler fitted, that of the MG Metro is cut to 0.39. The improvement does not sound dramatic, nor is it, but represents an improvement of five per cent—or, in my estimate, something like 1.5 mpg of petrol saved in high speed cruising. 'There are further gains to be made with a deeper front spoiler too', Steve Schlemmer comments, 'but that leads to clearance problems on ramps, or on uneven road surfaces, so we couldn't justify it to ourselves.' In fact there is an accessory spoiler available from BL Motorsport which many MG Metro customers will doubtless buy.

To make the car go quicker—to be able to exceed 100 mph and thus make it the fastest *ever* MG saloon car—an extra 15 per cent peak power was needed, for it had been decided to stick with the same wheel and tyre sizes and the same transmission as the 1.3GLS. Traditionally, this sort of power boost could be achieved with twin carburettors, and a more sporting camshaft, but for the MG Metro more subtle methods were used. Fred Coultas explained as follows: 'We wanted to use all the same basic running gear, and we found that by redeveloping the installation as a whole—manifolds, cylinder head and camshaft—we could get the extra power and keep a single SU carburettor'.

The heart of the engine lies in its breathing. For the MG version of the latest A-Plus engine, the compression ratio was increased to 10.5:1 (from 9.4:1), there were enlarged inlet valves and modified throats to suit and a different camshaft profile with increased 'overlap'. This, in fact, was even slightly more 'wild' than that fitted to the old Cooper S. It was all rounded off with lowered-friction pistons and a new water-heated inlet manifold, plus a rejetted carburettor, and such nicely thought-out details like a new type of 'sandwich' oil cooler fitted between the engine and the oil filter itself.

Outside the car, of course, there were MG octagons in evidence on all sides, but no separate grille as on the old-type MG 1100/1300 cars. The dominant feature of the exterior styling, apart from the rear spoiler, was the new type of road wheel, a light-alloy design from Wolfrace especially developed for BL Cars. It looked similar to the wheels to be found on the Metro Monaco and Frazer Tickford private venture models, but was subtly different in many ways. I could not help noting too, that on an MG, it was fitting that it should have eight cooling holes to each wheel!

Inside the car, there are controversial features like the red carpets and red safety belt webbings, but I doubt if any MG enthusiast would carp at the front seats, which look magnificent, hold the occupants firmly in place, and are as effective as any other sports seat I have ever tried. When the press were invited to drive the little MG Metro, I asked about the seats, and was told that they are basically standard Metro items, but with new top springing, padding and, of course, coverings. The result is quite outstanding.

But why, I asked, had not specialist seats, such as Recaros, been fitted instead? The answer astonished me: 'We tried Recaro seats at the prototype stage, and very good they were, but there was one big snag—it would have added £150 to the retail cost of the car. The seats we *have* used are all our own, they're as effective and as attractive, and they cost less than half that to the customer!'

To add to driver comforts, there is a small, 14 inch diameter, steering wheel with a padded leather rim, and specially styled instruments in a standard Metro 'pod', including a rev-counter reading up to 7,000 rpm, with a warning sector starting at 6,000 rpm. The foot rest fitted below the heater/radio console in the centre of the car looks useful but when I drove the car I found it rather awkwardly placed.

The nice thing about this new MG derivative of the Metro, as I found when I drove it for the first time, is that it is not merely a cosmetic job, but a nicely-integrated development which looks good, behaves well, and even sounds right because a big-bore exhaust system is fitted. The factory claim a top speed of 101 mph, and 0 – 60 mph acceleration of 10.9 seconds which make it a match for the old Mini-Cooper S (which could never reach 100 mph in standard form) and a real little 'fun' car to drive on the road.

No changes whatsoever were made to the suspension or braking systems of the basic Metro, though the new alloy wheels give a slightly broader base for the tyres to work on. It is as agile a car as the Mini-Cooper S ever was, with a much softer ride, greater refinement, and oceans more space inside. It would be nice, of course, to dream about even faster Metros, perhaps with higher gearing and a five-speed gearbox, but some of these dreams may already have been realised with a further Metro derivative to be announced in the near future.

How many can be sold? That, of course, is up to the customer, but even when the car was launched, BL's marketing staff were forecasting annual sales of 15,000 MGs a year in Great Britain alone (which is about 10 to 12 per cent of all forecast Metro sales) and its prospects in Europe, particularly in France and Italy, also looked to be extremely promising.

The real sales coup, as far as BL were concerned, was that both the MG Club chairman, Roche Bentley and Bill Wallis, placed orders for MG Metros even before they knew the price! Bentley said that he 'found the MG Metro fun to drive, especially as it handled so well. It is a sporty model in every sense of the word and I am delighted that the MG marque lives on in such a worthy car'. Wallis commented that: 'How good it is to see the MG marque back in the European market and especially as it is on such an appropriate vehicle with safe handling, allied to good performance. I hope we will go on to see many more MG models in the future'. He may get his wish!

But if neither of them knew the price when they ordered their cars, they must have been delighted when it was announced in May. Compared with the Metro 1.3HLS price of £4,948, and that of £5,150 for the sporty Ford Fiesta XR2 (and £5,750 for the even more upmarket Escort XR3) the MG Metro 1300 looked to be right on the spot at £4,799.

Compared with the MG Metro, however, the Metro Vanden Plas had an entirely different character. If the MG Metro was for the young blood, and the young at heart, the new Metro Vanden Plas model, somehow, was a much more gentle machine, almost for gentlemen (or ladies!) to own. It could be argued that some of the luxury features had been stuck on (and BL staff made no attempt to hide this) but there was the built-in refinement of the basic Metro design to start from, and there had been a general, and very tasteful, upgrading of trim, furnishings and equipment.

It was BMC who had built the Vanden Plas name up again, from the trough in which it found itself after the Second World War. Edwin and Roland Fox had sold out their North London company to Leonard Lord (at Austin) in 1946 and, for the next 13 years, the Vanden Plas business concentrated on building special coachwork for

Background photograph *The Vanden Plas' interior has individually-styled cloth-trimmed door panels, special reclining seats and other luxury fitments, including a padded-rim steering wheel.* **Inset** *The Metro Vanden Plas is mechanically identical with the 1.3HLS but has extra exterior styling touches and a completely retrimmed interior.*

JFC 299X

the large A125/A135 'mayoral' cars produced by Austin. The breakthrough came in 1959 when BMC produced a 'Vanden Plas Princess' version of the Austin A99 saloon, but the Princess 1100 of the early 1960s was even more popular.

Both the 1100/1300 cars (of which more than 28,000 were made) and the Allegro-based 1500/1750 Vanden Plas saloons had started life at Longbridge, but had been shipped down to Kingsbury, North London, for completion of trim, and for the installation of sumptuous leather-covered seats and other accessories. In the 1970s, however, there were increasing 'image' problems. The general public had been impressed by the styling of the 1100/1300 'Farina' Vanden Plas cars, but not at all as enthusiastic about the Allegro-based models, whose rounded lines did not as easily match up to the traditional type of Vanden Plas radiator grille. The whole thing was not helped by the fact that the Kingsbury factory was closed down in 1979, and the Vanden Plas Princess' final assembly process was moved to the MG factory at Abingdon. Then, to crown it all, the Abingdon factory itself was condemned, and the result was that the Allegro-based car went out of production before the end of 1980.

For a new car, based on the Metro, therefore, there was going to have to be a rebuilding of the Vanden Plas 'image', and there was going to be the need for very careful styling and equipment touches to make it attractive to the media and the customers. Fortunately, the Vanden Plas name had begun to spread to other cars in the modern BL range—to a prestigious Daimler saloon from 1972, to a top-of-the-line Rover for 1980 and, in 1982, to the front-drive Austin Ambassador. The last new model, incidentally, reunited the names of Austin and Vanden Plas, which had not featured on the same car since 1959.

Not only this, but a new method of building the cars would have to be arranged, for both Kingsbury and Abingdon had now been sold off. Accordingly, the Austin Metro Vanden Plas was to become the very first 'Vanden Plas' motor car ever to be completely built at Longbridge instead of being shipped out, partly finished.

Producing such a car is both a toil, and a delight, for a styling department. On the one hand, they are able to develop new colour schemes, include more extras and generally upgrade the specification of a basic car, without as many cost restrictions as usual. On the other hand, there are always barriers, such as a ban on developing new sheet metal styling, or expensive components like lamps, facia layouts and seat folding layouts, to compromise the whole deal.

The Vanden Plas derivative, however, was a delightfully satisfying little car to develop and the end result displayed discreet changes, nicely detailed additions, in a carefully integrated package. It might not be as obviously 'Vanden Plas' as previous BMC/BL small/medium cars had been, but it was clearly an attractive little car.

Mechanically, there were no surprises, but one important omission. In general, the 'chassis' and running gear of the Metro Vanden Plas were identical with that of the 1.3HLS (in other words, there had been no attempt to upgrade the performance like that of the MG Metro), which is to say that the usual 60 bhp 1,275 cc engine was fitted, with a 3.444:1 final drive ratio and four-speed manual gearbox, allied to the highly-developed Hydragas suspension and the sophisticated and very powerful braking system.

The omission which surprised me, however, was that automatic transmission was not to be made optional, for it had been a feature of previous 1100/1300 and Allegro-based models for well over a decade. When I queried this decision, at launch-time, I was told that market research did not identify enough demand to make the option necessary, and I was politely reminded that there already was a separate, and discrete, Metro Automatic model already. Even so, I'm happy to see that, in the months which followed, this policy was reversed.

Compared with the MG Metro, the Vanden Plas was different in so many detail ways. I was lucky to sample both models at the same pre-launch function, and was interested to see the subtle ways in which each car built up its own character. The Vanden Plas has even fewer recognition points on the exterior, compared with the MG Metro—a slightly different front grille, taped coach lines (and a tiny VP 'signature' on the rear flanks), and a bright 'Vanden Plas' badge on the hatchback is the only way to pick it out. There are, of course, the colours, not quite the same range as on other 1982-model Metros, and there is a very useful, and desirable, glass sun roof above the front seats, which is standard on the Vanden Plas, but optional on other Metros. This sunroof, incidentally, can not only be tilted open to increase ventilation, but can be removed altogether; it cannot be rolled back, as with other competitive designs.

The main attraction of the Vanden Plas car is in its interior and its special appointments. There is, of course, no more space, or stowage, than in the other Metros, but in general a great deal more money has been spent on the trim and detail equipment.

Like the MG Metro, the Vanden Plas car had bronze tinted glass all round but it did not have the bright carpets or the sporting instruments. BL's pre-launch publicity talked of 'unashamed luxury' (which used to be a TV advertising slogan for a particular brand of chocolate!) and drew attention to the special carpets, the thick-pile woven velvet seat upholstery and the traditionally ribbed cloth material used for door and rear quarter trims, not forgetting the walnut cappings to the doors and the carpet kick-strips on the doors themselves. There was even needle-cord carpet in the boot compartment and a new type of cloth headlining.

The instruments are standard Metro, but the steering wheel was a modified (14 inch diameter) version of that adopted for the MG Metro. As with the MG, a push-button radio with a digital read-out of selected frequencies was standard, and there were two loudspeakers, one in each door, rather than the single facia-mounted speaker fitted to other versions of the car.

All in all, it was a quiet, understated, somehow relaxed little car, as fast as the other normally-tuned 1.3-litre Metros, but with even more attention to fit, finish and a lack of commotion. Strangely enough, no extra sound-deadening treatment had been applied to the engine bay, but the extra interior trim made the car rather quieter than before. At the prototype stage, the MG Metro's large bore exhaust pipe had been assessed, but found to be not at all suitable for the Vanden Plas derivative.

It was not meant to be a mass-market version of the Metro and, at the price asked, £4,995, it could not be expected to flood through BL Cars showrooms. Nevertheless, forecasts of annual sales in Britain of between 6,500 and 10,000 cars a year were made when the car appeared—up to 200 cars a week out of Longbridge at full flood—which was more than had ever been achieved by the Vanden Plas Princesses finished off at the Kingsbury factory in the hey day of the earlier cars.

Brian Fox, operations director at Longbridge in 1982, says that the car goes down the assembly lines, but receives extra special attention in the Customer Validation Building, before being sent out through the normal checking and inspection system.

But the introduction of the MG and Vanden Plas derivatives did not even spell the last piece of Metro news in 1982, let alone in the life of the car. Even before the MG version had been made public, well-substantiated rumours began to appear in the

Neat, informative, but not ostentatious facia and instrument layout of the Metro. Things have certainly changed since the Mini was styled in 1959!

press, about a turbocharged MG Metro, to be made available in the autumn of 1982. This was not to be confused with the turbocharged engine conversions developed by BL Motorsport at Abingdon and Cowley, and already seen in the Wood and Pickett special Metros, nor with the astonishing rumours of 1981 which linked Williams Grand Prix Engineering with Rover V8 (or even V6!) engined Metros, with mid-engined Metros or even with four-wheel-drive Metros. Such a project, if it exists, would be a very costly, limited-production machine, intended to make BL competitive in the exotic world of World Championship Rallying.

The 'official' turbocharged MG Metro, to be launched in the autumn of 1982 after this book went to press, was to be a more civilised and infinitely more practical machine. It is interesting to realise that turbocharging had been chosen in preference to the development of a fuel-injected engine and there are very good reasons for this. VW, of course, were the first to produce a sporting small saloon (the Golf GTI) with fuel injection, mainly because they had close ties with Bosch, which made it all possible, while Ford also produced a fuel-injected version of their XR3 sports saloon, called RS1600i, on the 'me-too' basis.

In a confidential chat with me, about a year before the MG Metro Turbo was due to be seen, engineer Fred Coultas explained the company's thinking: 'I find that turbochargers are a very sensible approach to good breathing. In some cases, they have had rather a bad reputation, because they have been high-output, high-performance engines, but if you go for a relatively small turbo, you can make it work smoothly from a low speed range, which is what we have done.

'There isn't a lot of space in the engine bay, but we've found enough—just. We've mounted the turbocharger down at the side of the cylinder block, actually behind the engine as you view it from the front of the car, and arranged to by-pass feed it. Then we really *do* need more cooling air through the front grille, to keep it cool enough. With the sort of engine power output we wanted on the production car, we only need about seven to eight psi of turbocharger boost and we have developed an electronically controlled modulated system to produce the shape of torque curve needed'.

With a turbocharged engine, indeed, it would have been easy to over-stress the existing well-developed gearbox. In a private conversion, where some 'specialists' do not have to guarantee the long life of components not directly affected by their work, this might not have troubled the designers, but BL could not afford to be so cynical about it. Accordingly, you can be sure that a Metro Turbo will not be as powerful as it *could* be.

In one respect at least, the specification of the Metro Turbo was pre-empted by Harold Musgrove, and made public, months early. 'It's nice being a chairman sometimes', he told me. 'I marched into the styling studio one day late in 1981 to look at a mock-up of the Turbo on the floor, saw those beautiful seats and said: ''I like those. I want them on the MG in May''. I can get my way on things like that— and Brian Fox's people moved heaven and earth to get them ready for the MG in the spring, instead of for the Turbo in the autumn.'

At the time of writing, however, the Turbo, probably to carry the MG badge, was still in BL's future, a future which was beginning to look more exciting with every new model derivative to be announced. For the Metro, indeed, it promises to be a truly stimulating decade.

Chapter 10

Metro in the 1980s
. . . and beyond. A look into the future

As far as the motor car, and the motor industry, is concerned, it has been unwise for a pundit to make predictions. There is no way that we can know how economic conditions will have changed ten years hence, and we can only guess how motoring fashions will have developed. Is it even possible, therefore, to guess at the Metro's future? In the long term, or even in the short term? Will there be bigger ones, or smaller ones? Faster ones or slower ones? New styles, or new types?

It isn't easy, but I propose to have a go—and I ought to make one thing very clear. Everything so far written in this book about the life and times of the Metro has been hard fact—but *almost* everything you will read in this final chapter is pure speculation.

For the next few years, at least, the Metro's future looks to be secure. Even though major management (and perhaps corporate) changes were due to take place by the time this book was published, there wasn't likely to be a change in marketing philosophy. In its first two years the Metro proved to be a great success and it is obviously a range of cars which appeals to many people. Even after the initial rush of orders died away in 1981—when the rich vein of patriotism, and the latent 'Buy British' instincts had been tapped—there was still a massive and on-going demand for the little car.

For BL's visionaries, the stylists and the designers, the good news was that they seemed to have got their sums right in the 1970s, when they were having to plan years ahead. There was always an underlying worry in BL (though I found it difficult to get anyone to admit to it), that the Metro would no sooner be announced in 1980 than other companies would fight back with radically improved versions of their own 'Superminis', which had originally been launched in the 1970s. It hasn't happened yet. As hoped, the Metro has proved to be the first of the new wave of 'Superminis', and not the last of the originals. New cars announced since the arrival of Metro have gone some way to matching it, but none is out ahead, and starting a new race.

So, what happens next? For the next few years at least, the Metro is likely to consolidate its reputation and perhaps spawn off yet more derivations of the original design, rather than be replaced by a new design altogether. There are two very basic reasons for this—one being that of economics and one being because BL's planners are heavily occupied with other models in the ambitious recovery programme.

I am not betraying any closely-guarded secrets when I point out that BL Cars have been heavily involved in the development of a medium-sized range of cars ever since the Metro was ready to be released. When I was carrying out interviews for this book, my subjects repeatedly apologised for having rather rusty memories over events which had taken place three or four years earlier. 'Now, if you were asking me questions about LM10', Harold Musgrove said, with an engaging twinkle in his eyes, 'I would know all the answers, wouldn't I? But you'll have to wait. The LM10 story comes later.'

At this time, to everyone, the LM10/LM11 range had not been named, but by the time these words are read that decision will have been taken. This time it will be a range of cars with different body styles, and will be an ultra-modern replacement for the Maxi model (already dropped in 1981), the Allegro (disappearing during 1982) and eventually the Morris Ital.

After that, of course, there will be the new and (by repute) sensationally advanced Jaguar XJ40 model, and next, if things develop as BL Cars have forecast they will, will come the new 'executive' BL/Honda project. Which brings us up to 1985 at least, by which time the existing Metro will be five years old. By that time, who knows, the Mini may still be in production at Longbridge, or the Metro might have been joined by new versions, shapes, or layouts, of the same general mechanical design.

In the meantime, work on improving the Metro's design and its high level of quality and reliability, will go ahead unchecked. When I was talking to Fred Coultas about his team's work on the Metro, I asked him if there was ever any time to evaluate alternative materials, or ways of building the cars. 'Yes, the process is going on all the time', Fred said. 'For instance, with fuel economy in mind, we looked at the idea of using more light-alloy body panels, until we discovered that it was going to take a lot more energy *in total* (and therefore it was going to cost more) to make them instead of in steel. We would have had to charge you, the consumer, more, with the promise of marginally better fuel consumption figures. It didn't make marketing or engineering sense.

'Glass is heavy too, and even though we went down to 4 millimetres thickness from 5 millimetres on Metro (a saving of 20 per cent in weight), we considered going down more, to 3 millimetres. We abandoned that, not because it wasn't worth doing, but because the big panes were very fragile to handle, and we were breaking too many.' Even so, many changes have already been made, and will continue to be made, to make the Metro even better. As Fred Coultas says: 'The aluminium radiator is just a start!'.

When I last talked to Harold Musgrove, at a time when the Metro was fast approaching its first major mark, the production of the quarter-millionth example, he was relaxed, almost philosophical, about the car's future, and his own involvement in it: 'The Metro derivatives, the latest Rovers, the Ambassador and the LM10, they're all on time, all ready to go when planned. Now we have to worry about strategy for the company—I have to divorce myself, somewhat, from operational matters, to plan ahead with Ray Horrocks. I didn't have time to philosophise when we were preparing the Metro, now I *do* have time'.

Did he think, therefore, that Metro would be around for as long as the Mini had been? 'No, not that long, I'll be staggered if it is. Mini technology didn't change a lot in the 1960s and 1970s, but now its very different. By the end of the 1980s, perhaps, you're certainly going to see a lot more plastic in the car, very light weight panels coming in, you're certainly going to have electronic engine management, to control and optimise everything the engine does—switching cylinders out, controlling the idle, minimising the emissions, everything.

At the time of writing, I'm sure, no plan yet exists for the major redesigning of the Metro, for a car of the 1980s must have a long potential life to make profits for its makers. Certainly, when I asked Rex Fleming of the Styling Department if they had been asked to shape the car with a given 'life' in mind, he was emphatic that this was not so. 'You can't style a car—you *shouldn't* anyway—only to be fashionable for a fixed period. When we were working on ADO88, then on LC8, we were looking for a ''1980s car''.'

At which point Harris Mann, who was at the sharp end of the styling work on the car, chipped in with: 'Yes, and in the end it was also conceived as an ''International'' car, rather than a ''British'' car, which was what Mini had been'.

Tony Ball, in one of his most expansive moods, pointed out that no manufacturer was putting a car on sale these days unless he could be fairly sure of selling a lot of cars over a five to eight year period—'and even that's a very short period by today's standards'. Certainly the good old days of three-yearly restyling cycles at General Motors (in the 1960s) and four-year cycles at Ford (in the 1960s and 1970s) have gone for ever.

It seems certain, therefore, that the Metro, still recognisable as we know it today, will be around at Longbridge through the 1980s and probably into the early 1990s as well. Right now the struggle within the company is not to change the car itself, but to enlarge its markets, and to sell more and more of them. With the Austin Allegro out of production at Longbridge, CAB2 (the un-modernised Car Assembly Building to the east of the Metro/Mini building) has become vacant. As Harold Musgrove told me: 'If we really wanted to have a go these days, we could produce up to 8,000 cars a week from New West Works, and that's for 80 hours' operation only, by the way'.

In 1982, as these words are being written, BL's morale is on the up and up, and the most surprising predictions are being made. With Metro selling well, LM10 preparing to come on stream, and the Honda-based Triumph Acclaim doing even better than expected, the UK market share seems to be on the up-and-up. From a miserable 15 per cent of the British market in the bad old days of 1979/1980, BL's share jumped back to more than 20 per cent as the Metro took a hold on its market sector.

Now things are looking up even further. On the eve of the signing of the vitally important agreement between trade unions and management in the spring of 1982, Roger Eglin had this to say in *The Sunday Times*: 'The tantalising sales targets— 25 per cent of the British market, and 200,000 cars a year in Europe—have become more than just a gleam in BL's crystal ball . . . Success demands a slight softening of the pound, good production runs and freedom from the sort of disputes that have undermined buyers' confidence in the past. But the most important weapon in winning the extra sales, the new models, are beginning to pop out of BL like peas from a pod. There have been 20 major model changes or launches in the past 18 months and the pace is warming up'.

The key to sales expansion, and to the need to assemble more Metros, or different types, is not Britain, where there are practical limits to the number of small hatchbacks which can find customers, but is Europe. For years, in the late 1970s and early 1980s, British manufacturers in general, not merely BL Cars, were in retreat. BL European sales slipped to 80,000, a figure matched by sales to Britain *alone* by competitors like Renault and the VW/Audi Group, but now they are on the way up

Rear view, hatch open, of a 1982-model Metro and the 1.3S with its hatch closed. The word 'mini' is now no longer evident in the rear badging.

again. BL sales and marketing director, Trevor Taylor, believes that the improvement is permanent, and will continue.

As the 1980s progress, my guess is that we shall eventually see new derivatives of the Metro introduced, not merely those with different trim packs, different marketing approaches or different engines, like the City, MG 1300 and Vanden Plas of 1982, but those with styling changes or additions. Perhaps I should skim over the persistent rumour of a really startling limited-production (200-off is all the regulations require) Metro from BL Motorsport, with outright wins in International rallying in mind. The time must surely come when changes to what the Americans call 'the sheet metal'—to the shape and the make-up of the body itself—can be considered.

In this case it is easy to speculate on what could be done, even though BL have done no more than confirm that certain courses of action are feasible, if not probable. The three obvious paths to be considered are that of producing an estate car version of the car (coupled with a van, for commercial vehicle purposes), a five-door derivative of the basic three-door design, or of converting the style into something looking like a conventional 'three-box' booted version of the saloon Metro.

There are precedents in every case, though in no case was the company concerned as far advanced in the technology of building bodies as is BL Cars with New West Works at Longbridge. Renault, for instance, produced a five-door version of the three-door Renault 5 some years later, though the two cars had been styled and engineered together, while VW and Honda have both derived booted saloon cars from hatchback designs. BL's own Triumph Acclaim, for instance, is really a Honda Ballade, which is a longer, booted version of the latest hatchback Civic model.

Would there be a demand for any such type of modified Metro, if it could be put on the market, I wondered? Tony Ball was saying little, but spelt out the possibilities succinctly: 'Which makes more sense to us in terms of sales? I've got to answer that in two ways—there is no doubt that there is still a conservative sector of the public, certainly the fleet users, who need and like a separate locking boot, so there will always be a demand for that. However, the trends, the tendencies, are towards retaining a hatchback. The Austin Ambassador is a hatchback when the Princess wasn't, and the Ford Sierra is a hatchback when the Cortina wasn't. There's no doubt that in terms of practical usage, a hatchback has immense practical value'.

He also confirmed what had often been rumoured in magazines and newspapers, that the new medium-size BL range of cars to be built at Cowley would include LM10, which is a hatchback, and LM11, which is a 'conventional' booted car. He also said (and the published figures prove his point) that the demand for hatchbacks is proportionally greatest at the Metro end of the market.

Stephen Schlemmer, the staff director in charge of Product Planning, also confirms that his colleagues have looked very carefully at the figures: 'We do a lot, really a lot, of analyses of the market place. It's largely a question of numbers, numbers sold. We look at trends in wheelbases, trends in widths and trends in body types. We see, for instance, that the VW Derby (now the Polo Classic in its new style) booted hatchback concept of the Polo hasn't worked anything like so well for VW as the five-door version of the Renault 5 has worked for the French. We've considered a booted notchback Metro and couldn't justify the investment to ourselves. We would find the idea of a five-door Metro much more promising'.

Having been told that, I felt free to go back to Rex Fleming of the styling department and ask him if a notchback had been considered? 'It certainly could be done, just as VW produced the Derby from the Polo. In fact when the notchback Derby appeared, early in 1977, which was when we were well down the road on the Metro project, we had a brief look at the concept, and built up a couple of clay models. Eventually we went to management and said, ''Yes, we can notchback the car if we have to, but it would take a great deal of work, and take us away from the integrated design of the present car''. In terms of investment it wouldn't be too terrifying, but it would be a big challenge to the technology in the body factory at Longbridge'.

This sort of contingency, however, had already been identified, even before the highly-automated assembly plant had been put in to the New West Works at Longbridge. When I last toured the facility, my guides had been careful to point out that there was still considerable flexibility in the way the shells could be put together. Tony Gilroy, who had the awesome responsibility for the installation and working-up of the new facilities, made it clear that it would have been very foolish *not* to allow for some sort of change, or addition, to the original concept. Otherwise, when the time came to react to market pressures, an enormous carve-up would have been required.

'Of course we thought about it', Gilroy said. 'Certain facilities are fairly rigid—you'd probably not want to change the floor pan, for instance—but the paint shops, the conveyors and the assembly lines could all deal with cars which were slightly longer, or different, perhaps. Where we would have a problem, no doubt, would be with the body monosides. But that's a pressings problem, only. The bit where it *is* difficult is where we do the automatic body framing—where the floor meets the sides, the roof and so on. But there are gaps in that fixture—dwell stations, we call them—where the bodies move between welding sequences. In those stations, new fixtures could be installed and you wouldn't have to disturb or destroy the existing tooling. When it comes to the automatic welding—no, there's no problem there. All that would have to be done is to re-programme the Unimate robots.' Damned clever, these computers . . ..

But, in reality, I detected no definite and concrete plans for Metro's future when I was closely involved in the preparation of this book. Now, more than at any time in recent years, BL management is 'thinking on its feet'—the speed with which the Metro City was introduced in 1982 proves that. As the total Longbridge workforce reduced slightly in 1981/1982, production marginally increased. Figures released in March 1982 showed that the workforce declined from 15,000 to 13,500 while production went up from 5,867 to 6,100 cars a week in all.

The changes which *might* be introduced in the next few years at BL Cars were deftly summed up by Ray Horrocks when asked about new investment later in the 1980s: 'Who wants a giant press shop, when the future is in lines of injection moulding machines going squirt, squirt?'

Even as these final words were being written, BL Cars' corporate shape was changing again. Austin-Morris, having evolved in the LMC (Light Medium Cars) division, was renamed Austin-Rover, and it also became clear what future naming policies would involve. As the 1980s progresses, the 'Austin' and 'Rover' marques will come to dominate, though 'Morris' will be retained for some time. Marques like 'Triumph', 'MG' and 'Vanden Plas' will also persist, but mainly as up-market versions of the latest Austins and Rovers.

All in all, if I had been writing a book about British Leyland in the mid-1970s, I would have been very worried about the future. At this point in BL Cars' development, however, the prospects are very different. At times it may be a bumpy ride, but it's going to be exhilarating as well. When we look back on BL from the year 2000, we might identify the Metro as the car which started the recovery process. And if it was, it will have deserved it. Tony Ball's patriotic slogan might have to be modified to: 'A British car *company* to beat the world'.

Index

Note: To keep this index to a manageable length, it has not been possible to note every BMC/BL model which appears in the text. However, each car closely related to the Metro, in size or price, *has* been mentioned. There are so many references to the BL Mini cars that no attempt has been made to index this car either.

In the case of people whose titles changed over the years, their final titles appear in this index.

Illustration caption references are printed in **bold** type.

The Metro in side view, showing a smooth underside, and a complete lack of pointless decoration.